Smot
a Swyn
y Nadolig

Eric Hill

Roedd Sam, tad Smot, yn llanw basgedaid o goed. 'Helô, ro'n i'n meddwl dy fod ti'n addurno'r goeden.'

'Mae'r tinsel ar y goeden wedi cynhyrfu, Dad.'

Gwenodd Sam. 'Dyna beth sy'n digwydd adeg y Nadolig.'

Yna meddai llais dierth. 'Hm! Esgusodwch fi. Helô.' Edrychodd Smot a Sam i bobman. O'r diwedd fe welson nhw ben yn edrych i lawr dros y ffens.

'Ydych chi wedi gweld sled?'

'Sled mawr coch.' Daeth pen arall i'r golwg dros y ffens.

'Sled hud Santa,' meddai'r ddau ben gyda'i gilydd. 'Rhaid i Santa gael y sled erbyn heno.'

'Chi yw ceirw Santa?' gofynnodd Smot.

'Ie, ond rŷn ni wedi colli'r sled. Os na chawn ni afael arno, fydd 'na ddim anrhegion i neb.'

'Ond mae hynna'n ofnadwy!' meddai Smot. 'Beth allwch chi wneud?'

'Dal ati i chwilio,' meddai'r ceirw yn drist.
Ac fe ddiflannodd y ddau i'r coed.

Roedd Smot yn ddiflas iawn.

'Helpa nhw, Smot. Cer at dy ffrindiau a gofyn ydyn nhw wedi gweld y sled,' awgrymodd Sam.

'Fe a' i'n syth at Elen,' meddai Smot.

Roedd Elen yn gwneud bisgedi yn y gegin. '*Iw-hw! Elen!*' gwaeddodd Smot. Neidiodd Elen a neidiodd yr eisin hefyd.

'Elen, mae sled Santa ar goll ac rwy'n helpu i chwilio amdano. Wyt ti wedi'i weld e?'

'Sled mawr coch yw e?'

'Ie, ie!'

'Ro'n i'n meddwl. Na, 'dwy ddim wedi'i weld e. Gofynna i Tom. Fe ddo i helpu ar ôl i fi orffen fy ngwaith.'

'Iawn,' meddai Smot. 'Ga i un o'r bisgedi?'

'Dŷn nhw ddim yn barod,' meddai Elen. Ond roedd Smot wedi mynd.

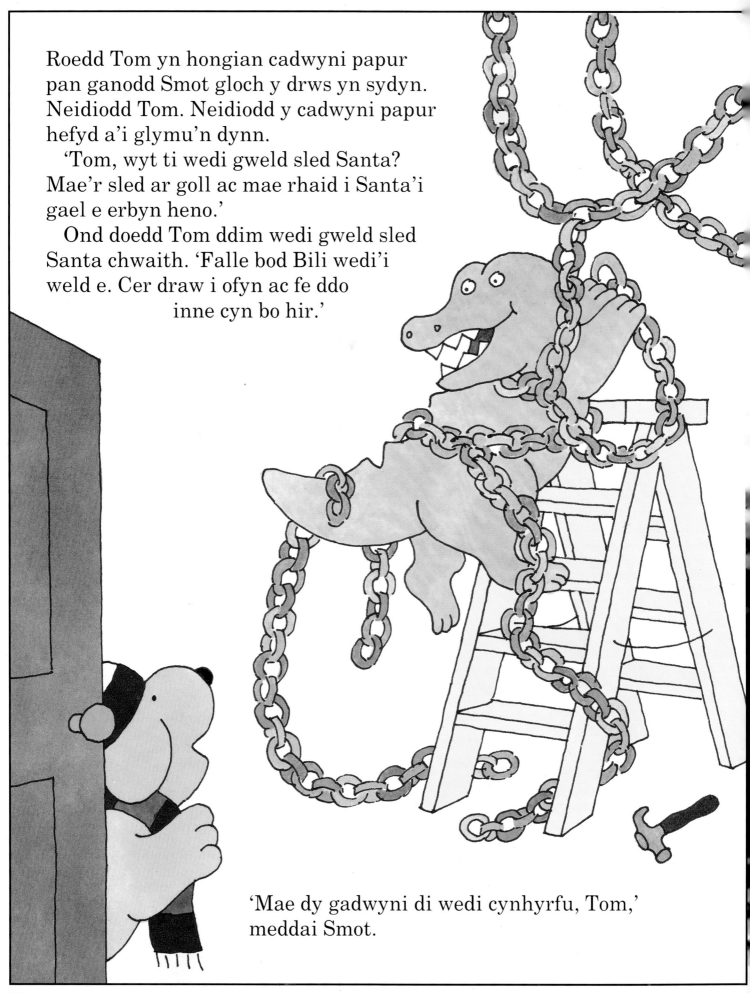

Roedd Tom yn hongian cadwyni papur
pan ganodd Smot gloch y drws yn sydyn.
Neidiodd Tom. Neidiodd y cadwyni papur
hefyd a'i glymu'n dynn.

'Tom, wyt ti wedi gweld sled Santa?
Mae'r sled ar goll ac mae rhaid i Santa'i
gael e erbyn heno.'

Ond doedd Tom ddim wedi gweld sled
Santa chwaith. 'Falle bod Bili wedi'i
weld e. Cer draw i ofyn ac fe ddo
inne cyn bo hir.'

'Mae dy gadwyni di wedi cynhyrfu, Tom,'
meddai Smot.

10

'Bili, Bili, wyt ti 'na?' galwodd Smot wrth ysgwyd y bocs llythyron.
Roedd Bili'n lapio pêl fawr hardd, ei anrheg Nadolig i Smot.
Neidiodd e a neidiodd y bêl a sboncio dros y lle. 'Aros funud,'
gwaeddodd Bili. O'r diwedd fe yrrodd e'r bêl i mewn i'r cwpwrdd.
'Dere i mewn, Smot. Mae'r drws ar agor.'

Soniodd Smot am helynt sled Santa.
''Dwy i ddim wedi gweld sled mawr coch,' meddai Bili. 'Ond
rwy *wedi* gweld sled bach glas.'
'Ble?'
'Fan hyn. Fy sled glas i yw e.
Dere am reid.'

'Fe ddylen ni chwilio am sled Santa ond . . . o'r gore 'te,
falle y gallwn ni chwilio a chwarae ar yr un pryd.'
Gwthiodd Smot a Bili'r sled i ben rhiw hir
ac eisteddon nhw arno.
'Cydia'n dynn, Smot!'
Dechreuodd y sled gyflymu.
Daeth Elen a Tom i'r golwg
ar waelod y rhiw.
'Symuda hi, Elen!
Symuda hi, Tom!'

Gwibiodd y sled i lawr y rhiw a stopio'n sydyn mewn pentwr o eira meddal.

'Hwrê! Alla i gael reid arall, Bili?'

'Mae Tom a fi wedi chwilio ym mhobman am sled Santa, ond does 'na ddim sôn amdano,' meddai Elen. 'Ydych chi wedi'i weld e?'

'Arhoswch funud,' meddai Bili. 'Beth sy yn y coed draw fan'na?'

Roedd rhywbeth coch yn cuddio rhwng y llwyni.

'O da iawn, Bili!' meddai Tom.
  'Ond nid sled Santa yw hwnna,' meddai Smot.
  'Na, fy mhêl i yw hi,' meddai Tom. 'Collais i'r bêl
echdoe. Dyna lwcus!'

'Gawn ni fynd ar y sled nawr?' gofynnodd Elen.
  'Wrth gwrs,' meddai Bili. 'Ond peidiwch
â bod yn hir.'
  'A chwiliwch am sled Santa,'
meddai Smot.

'Mae dy sled di'n wych,' meddai Smot. 'Dw i eisiau sled
fel hwnna.'

   'Gofynna i Santa ddod ag un i ti,' meddai Bili.

   'Mae'n rhy hwyr,' meddai Smot. 'Ta beth, chawn ni *ddim byd*
gan Santa eleni, os na ddown ni o hyd i'r sled coch.'

Gwibiodd Elen a Tom i lawr y rhiw.

   'Whiiiii! Dyna hwyl!' meddai Elen.

   'Doedd dim sôn am sled Santa,'
meddai Tom.

   'Fe gawn ni un reid fach arall,'
meddai Bili. 'Dere ymhellach
i lawr y rhiw.'

'Neidiwch ar y sled, chi'ch dau,' meddai Elen. 'Fe wthiwn ni chi.'

'Un, dau, tri, *ffwrdd â chi!*' Gwthiodd Tom ac Elen â'u holl nerth a gwibiodd y sled i lawr y rhiw yn gynt a chynt. Stopiodd e ddim nes cyrraedd i ganol y coed.

'Wawww!' meddai Smot. 'Dyna beth oedd reid hir. Ond, Bili, *edrycha draw fan'na!*'

Trodd Bili i edrych. 'Elen! Tom! Dewch i weld beth sy gyda ni!'

'Mae e'n fawr iawn,' meddai Elen.
'Ac yn goch iawn,' meddai Tom.
'Hwnna yw sled Santa,' meddai Bili.

'Wel,' meddai Smot, 'nawr mae rhaid i ni gael gafael ar y ceirw. Fe a' i i ddweud wrth Dad.'

'Mae'n bryd i ni i gyd fynd adre,' meddai Elen. 'Ond bydd dy dad yn gwybod beth i'w wneud.'

'Pob lwc, Smot!' galwodd ei ffrindiau wrth i Smot fynd i ffwrdd.

Roedd Dad yn gorffen llwytho'r coed tân.

'Rŷn ni wedi cael gafael ar y sled, Dad. Mae e yn y coed.'

'Bobol bach! Ardderchog!'

'Ond sut galla i gael gafael ar y ceirw a dweud wrthyn nhw?'

'Dilyna ôl eu traed, wrth gwrs!'

Roedd dwy res glir o olion traed yn yr eira. 'Mae hyn yn hawdd,'
meddai Smot. Plygodd ei ben dros yr olion a rhedodd yn igam-ogam
mewn cylch rownd y coed nes oedd ei ben yn troi. Yn sydyn, *clec!*
—trawodd yn erbyn dwy goes hir iawn.

'Mae'n ddrwg gen i, rwy'n chwilio am . . . amdanoch *chi!*'
'Rwyt ti wedi cael gafael arnon ni,' meddai'r carw cyntaf.
'Ac rwy wedi cael gafael ar y sled,' meddai Smot.
'Ardderchog! Neidia ar fy nghefn i a dangosa'r ffordd i ni.'

'Mae hyn yn well na'r sled hyd yn oed,' meddai Smot.
   'Ond mae sled mawr Santa'n well o lawer,' meddai'r ceirw.
'Wyt ti am reid?'
   'O, *ydw*,' meddai Smot. 'Edrychwch. Rŷn ni'n pasio tŷ ni.
Gadewch i fi ofyn i Dad.'

Doedd Sam ddim yn siŵr. 'Mae mor hwyr, Smot.'
   'Fyddwn ni ddim yn hir,' meddai'r carw cyntaf.
   'Fyddwn ni ddim chwinc,' meddai'r ail garw.
   'O'r gore, Smot, gan ei bod hi'n Nadolig,' meddai Sam.
'Ond gofala dy fod ti gartre cyn nos.'
   'Diolch, Dad,' meddai Smot.

Roedd y sled fel newydd. Roedd y ceirw'n falch
dros ben.
'Dringa i mewn, Smot. I ffwrdd â ni!'

Cyflymodd y sled wrth ddod allan
o'r coed a hedfanodd dros yr eira.
Gwelodd Smot ei gartref
a'r goeden Nadolig
yn y ffenest.

21

Yn sydyn roedden nhw'n uchel yn yr awyr.
Edrychai cartref Smot fel tegan bach.
Gwelodd e gartrefi Tom ac Elen a Bili
a'r wlad i gyd oddi tano. Tywyllodd
yr awyr a disgleiriodd golau ym mhob tŷ
drwy'r pentref i gyd.

Yna edrychodd Smot i fyny.
  'O! Y sêr!'
  'Mae e'n hoffi'r sêr,'
meddai'r carw cyntaf.
  'Y sêr amdani 'te,'
meddai'r carw arall.
  Cododd y sled mewn
hanner cylch i'r awyr
a syrthiodd y sêr
yn gawod ddisglair
o'u hamgylch.

'Mynyddoedd o'n blaen!'
galwodd y ceirw.
   'Dyna beth od!' meddai Smot.
'Does dim mynyddoedd
ffordd hyn.'
   Ond wir, codai rhes
o fynyddoedd yn
syth o'u blaen.

Arafodd y sled wrth fynd drwy'r cwm rhwng y mynyddoedd.
Ym mhen pella'r cwm roedd ogof yn y graig. Hedfanodd y sled
yn syth i mewn.

   Agorodd Smot ei geg yn syn. Doedd e erioed wedi gweld
cymaint o fynd a dod.

'O! Gweithdy Santa!' meddai Smot. Y funud honno daeth Santa i'r golwg drwy dwll yn y graig a chododd ei law ar Smot. 'Alla i ddim credu hyn,' meddai Smot.

 'Mae'n bryd i ti fynd adre nawr,' meddai'r ceirw. 'Mae gyda ni noson brysur heno.'

Gadawodd y sled yr ogof a'r mynyddoedd.
Hedfanodd drwy'r sêr at bentre Smot
a glanio'n ymyl y tŷ.

'O, diolch,' meddai Smot. 'Roedd hwnna fel . . . fel swyn.'
    'Mae'r Nadolig yn llawn o hud a swyn,' meddai'r ceirw.

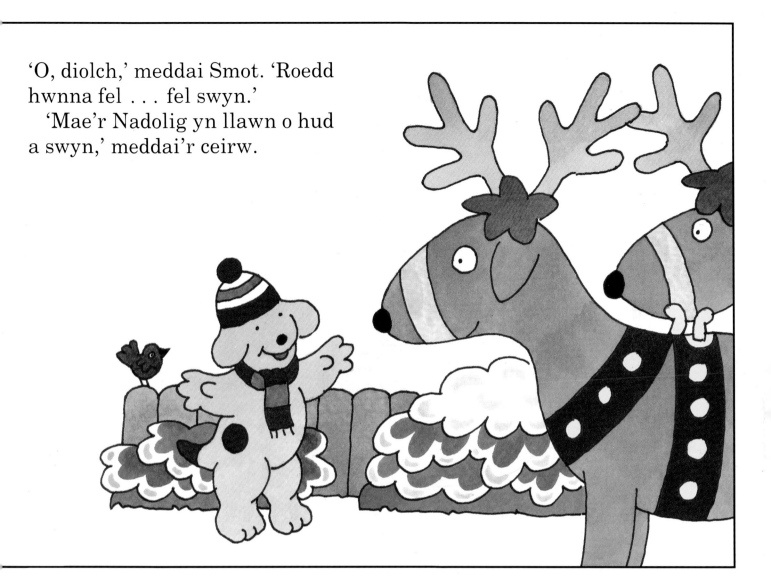

Edrychodd Smot i'r awyr. Roedd hi'n olau dydd o hyd. Doedd dim sôn am y sêr.
    Pan drodd e at y ceirw, roedden nhw a'r sled wedi diflannu.

Roedd Sam yn dal i sefyll yn yr union fan wrth
y pentwr coed. 'Helô, Smot. Ro'n i'n meddwl dy fod
ti'n mynd am reid.'
  'Rwy wedi bod, Dad. Roedd e'n wych.'
  'Fuest ti ddim yn hir,' meddai Sam.
  'Naddo wir,' meddai Smot.

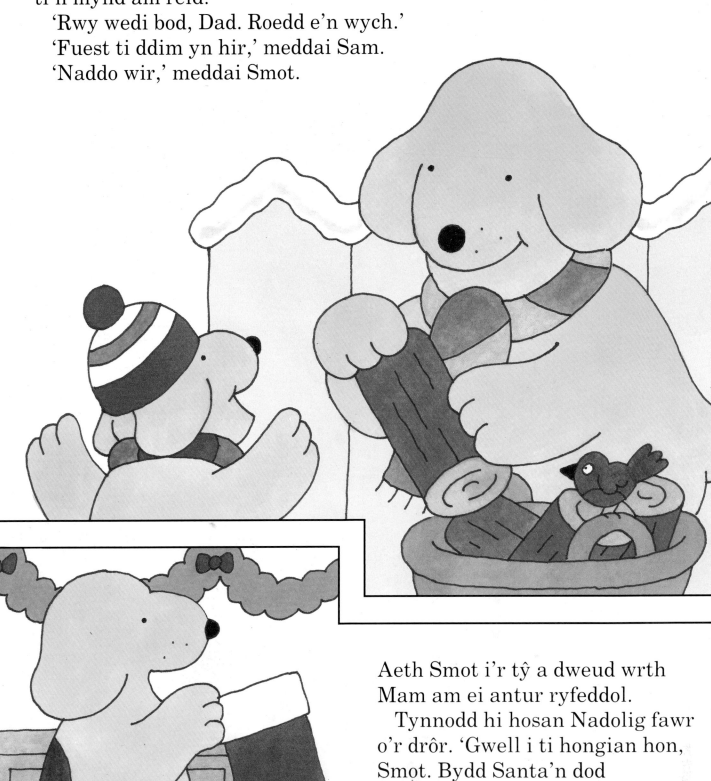

Aeth Smot i'r tŷ a dweud wrth
Mam am ei antur ryfeddol.
  Tynnodd hi hosan Nadolig fawr
o'r drôr. 'Gwell i ti hongian hon,
Smot. Bydd Santa'n dod
cyn bo hir.'

Edrychodd Smot drwy'r ffenest ar awyr y nos.
  'Rwy'n gwybod, Mam,' meddai.
  Ac am eiliad, rhwng y sêr fry uwchben, gwelodd e'r ddau garw
a Santa yn ei sled mawr coch.

Ac yn y bore
roedd un parsel arall
arbennig iawn
i Smot . . .

I Smot
oddi wrth
x x x
X X

FACTIVITY®

TRAVEL THROUGH THE AMAZING WORLD OF WILD ANIMALS

This edition published by Parragon Books Ltd in 2016

Parragon Books Ltd
Chartist House
15–17 Trim Street
Bath BA1 1HA, UK
www.parragon.com

Written by Steve Parker
Edited by Grace Harvey
Consultant: Gerald Legg, PhD

Illustrated by Genie Espinosa
Designed by Duck Egg Blue and Alex Dimond

ISBN 978-1-4748-6268-4

Printed in China

FACTIVITY

TRAVEL THROUGH THE AMAZING WORLD OF WILD ANIMALS

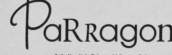

PaRragon

Bath • New York • Cologne • Melbourne • Delhi
Hong Kong • Shenzhen • Singapore

Contents

What is an animal?

Animals come in all shapes, sizes and colours. Some are almost too small to see. Others are as huge as a house. But they all have some things in common.

Animals make babies, or **breed**. Some animal mothers lay eggs, others give birth to live young.

Animals **move**. They might walk, run, jump, crawl, creep, climb, slither, burrow, flap, fly, swoop or swim!

Animals need to **eat**. Some animals are plant-eaters. Others are meat-eaters. Some eat almost anything.

Baby animals **grow**. Some take just a few weeks to grow into adults, others take many years.

Animals use their **senses** to find out about the world around them. Eyes see, ears hear, noses smell, tongues taste and skin feels.

Animal kingdom

There are millions of different animals! Scientists use their features, such as number of legs, to group them into types. This helps us understand them better.

All animals

The animal kingdom is split into two main groups: **vertebrates** and **invertebrates**.

Humans are animals too!

Vertebrates

A vertebrate is an animal with a backbone. There are five kinds of vertebrates: **mammals**, **birds**, **reptiles**, **amphibians** and **fish**.

Invertebrates

An invertebrate is an animal without a backbone. This group includes insects, spiders, crabs, snails, worms and many others.

The giant spider crab has a hard shell.

Insects, like the darkling beetle, have six legs.

The giant earthworm is long, squishy and wriggly.

Spiders, like the tarantula, have eight legs.

Mammals

- ✔ Warm-blooded
- ✔ Covered by fur or hairs
- ✔ Mothers feed their babies on milk

Birds

- ✔ Warm-blooded
- ✔ Covered by feathers, with wings and a beak
- ✔ Lay eggs that hatch into chicks

Reptiles

- ✔ Cold-blooded
- ✔ Scaly skins
- ✔ Most lay eggs, some give birth to babies

Fish

- ✔ Cold-blooded
- ✔ Gills to breathe underwater, fins for swimming
- ✔ Lay eggs

Amphibians
- ✔ Cold-blooded
- ✔ Lay eggs in water
- ✔ Begin life with gills
- ✔ Develop lungs as they grow into adults in order to live on land

? Which types of animals do these body parts belong to?

....

What's a habitat?

A habitat is an animal or plant's home. It is the place that provides the right conditions, such as food, temperature and amount of water, for that living being.

Tropical rainforests grow in warm, wet areas around the Equator.

Deserts may be covered in sand, pebbles or rocks, but they are all dry. It may not rain for many years.

I think I live in a temperate woodlands habitat!

Temperate woodlands are found in areas where there are cold winters and warm summers. Most trees are deciduous (they lose their leaves in winter).

? What type of habitat do you think you live in?

....

10

The **polar regions** are in the far north and far south of the world. In winter, the sea can be covered with thick sheets of ice and snow.

Tundra is areas of northern land that are frozen for most of the year. It is too cold for trees to grow.

Conifer forests grow in cold parts of the world. Most of the trees have cones rather than blossom and are evergreen (they have leaves all year round).

The Equator is an imaginary line running around the centre of the world.

Grasslands are in warm or hot places where there is not enough rain for trees to grow.

The water in **seas and oceans** is salty. They vary from warm to cold, shallow to deep.

The water in **rivers and lakes** is not salty. Some are no more than a trickle, others are huge!

Tropical rainforests

Rainforests are hot and wet. These are ideal conditions for life. There are more kinds of animals and plants in tropical rainforests than anywhere else in the world!

Most rainforest life is high in the canopy.

The **boa constrictor** waits in the tree. It is looking for a victim to coil around, squeeze to death and swallow whole. Then it won't feed again for weeks.

The **jaguar** prowls along the forest floor, its claws and teeth ready to kill. Its cats' eyes see well in the dark, and it listens and sniffs for prey.

The **scarlet macaw** loves the sunshine at the top of the tallest trees. This big, bright parrot's strong beak easily cracks nuts and seeds.

The **howler monkey** hangs out in the tangle of upper branches (the canopy). It is well named, because its huge howls and noisy roars carry far through the forest.

The **poison dart frog** sits, unafraid, in the lower branches (the understorey). Its bright colours warn others: Don't try to eat me. I'm poisonous!

Some animals have colours and patterns that blend into the forest.

Can you spot a...

red-eyed green tree frog?

owl butterfly?

emerald tree boa snake?

On the move

Rainforests are crowded with tree trunks, branches, twigs, leaves, flowers and fruits. Creatures have many ways of moving around.

Who's flying high?

The harpy eagle soars above the trees, flapping and gliding. It dives to grab tasty food such as a monkey, sloth or bird.

Who's the best climber?

The spider monkey uses its curly tail as an extra limb to hold on as it climbs from one branch to another.

Who parachutes?

The flying frog has big flaps of skin (webs) between its extra-long toes. It's like having four parachutes!

Who's a speedy crawler?

The centipede has over 50 legs. It races along by wriggling its body with a wave-like motion.

Who makes huge jumps?

The bushbaby suddenly straightens its long legs and springs into mid air to catch a yummy moth or fly.

Fold and unfold
in half lengthways.

Fold and unfold
top corners down.

Turn paper over.
Now fold and unfold
through the diagonals.

Turn paper over. Now
pull the sides down
and into the centre.

Fold these points
upwards to make
the front legs.

Fold sides into
the centre.

Fold up.

Fold down.

To make him
jump, press down
on his back!

15

Toucan

It's one of the biggest beaks, for the size of body, of any bird!

Inside its huge beak, the toucan has a tongue that is nearly as long, and just right for scooping out the soft middle of fruits.

The toucan's huge beak looks weighty. But inside it's filled with hollows of air, like a sponge. This makes it lighter.

The toucan's big eyes help it choose fruits that are ripe, juicy and ready to eat by seeing what colour they are.

Toucans can be noisy! They make doggy barks and froggy croaks, and make clapping sounds by snapping their beaks together.

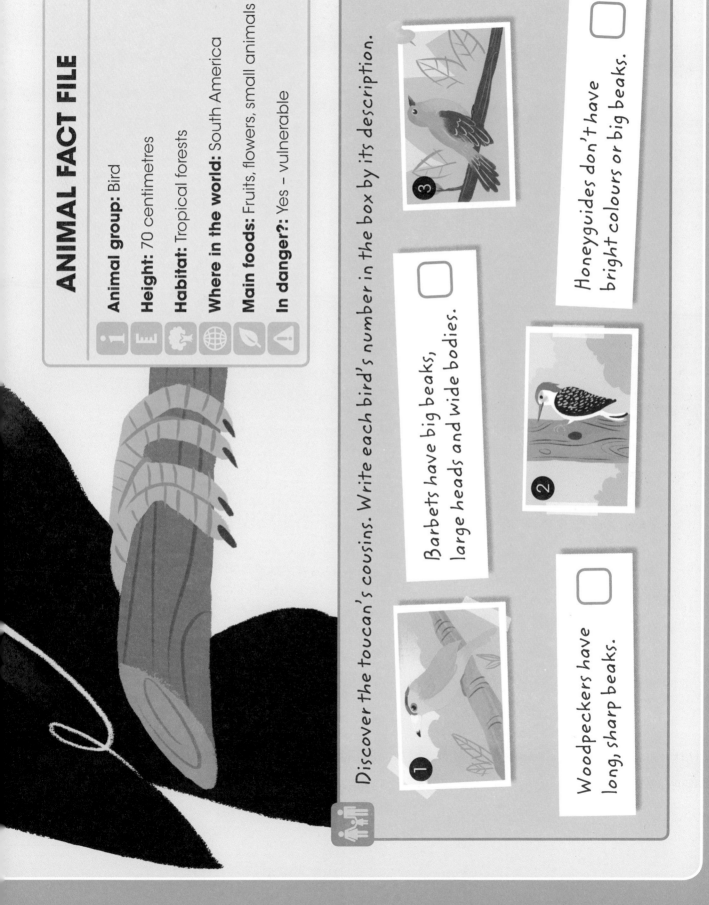

ANIMAL FACT FILE

Animal group: Bird

Height: 70 centimetres

Habitat: Tropical forests

Where in the world: South America

Main foods: Fruits, flowers, small animals

In danger?: Yes – vulnerable

Discover the toucan's cousins. Write each bird's number in the box by its description.

Barbets have big beaks, large heads and wide bodies.

Honeyguides don't have bright colours or big beaks.

Woodpeckers have long, sharp beaks.

Out of sight

Look quickly around the rainforest. At first, you might not see any creatures. But they are there. They are disguised as their surroundings, using a clever trick called camouflage.

Prey animals use camouflage to avoid being seen by predators!

A lump of slimy bird dropping is not what most animals want to eat. But look closer. It's actually a **bird-dropping caterpillar** in disguise.

If a **stick insect** sees a predator, it stays completely still, so it looks like the twigs around it.

Tawny frogmouths fly around at night to catch moths and flies. By day, they sleep on branches. Their patchy brown feathers resemble tree bark.

Colour the chameleon to make it blend into its surroundings!

The **flower mantis** has wide petal-like flaps on its body and legs. When a small insect comes near, the mantis grabs it!

An **Amazon horned frog** waits in piles of brown leaves, with only its head sticking out, before springing out to swallow its prey!

Yes, and predators use camouflage to sneak up on prey!

19

Orang-utan

ANIMAL FACT FILE

 Animal group: Mammal

 Height: 1.5 metres

 Habitat: Tropical forests

 Where in the world: South-East Asia

 Main foods: Fruits, leaves, grubs

 In danger?: Yes – endangered

The orang-utan's teeth are sharp and strong. They can pull the tough skins off fruits and crack hard seeds.

An adult male has wide cheek flaps called flanges. These make him look big and strong to females.

Long fur allows rain to drip off easily. In heavy downpours, this ape may even hold a big leaf over itself as an umbrella.

The clever orang-utan uses thick leaves like gloves to protect its hands when picking up spiky fruit.

Can you pick a pencil up using your toes? Orang-utans are able to do this easily because their big toes can touch the other toes on the same foot, just like our thumbs can touch the other fingers on the same hand.

It's harder than it looks!

The orang-utan's legs bend in a similar way to the arms, and the feet grip branches just as well as the hands.

Monkey or ape?

The rainforest is noisy with the chattering, whoops and shouts of monkeys and apes. These mammals are similar in many ways, but different in others. They both belong to the animal group called primates.

SPOTTERS' GUIDE: APES

- ✔ Apes live only in Africa and Asia
- ✔ There are about 20 different kinds of ape
- ✔ Good senses, especially big eyes for detailed vision
- ✔ No tail
- ✔ Fingers hold small objects well
- ✔ Large, heavy body, often upright

SPOTTERS' GUIDE: MONKEYS

- ✔ Monkeys live in Europe, Africa, Asia and the Americas
- ✔ There are over 250 different kinds of monkey
- ✔ Good senses, including keen sense of smell
- ✔ Tail to help with balance
- ✔ Fingers suited to holding larger objects
- ✔ Small, light body, usually horizontal

You're on safari! Check your spotters' guides to work out which animals are monkeys and which are apes! Write the answers below.

Clue:
Native to South and Central American forests

....

Clue:
The largest and heaviest living primate

....

Clue:
Can easily hold small objects, like fruits

....

Clue:
Uses its tail for balance when swinging through the trees

....

King cobra

Animal group: Reptile

Length: 5.5 metres

Habitat: Tropical forests

Where in the world: South and South-East Asia

Main foods: Snakes, lizards, rats

In danger?: Yes – vulnerable

One king cobra has enough venom to kill 20 people. Stay away!

Cobras have flaps of skin on the neck, which they spread out into a hood when they are angry.

The king cobra makes a lightning-fast bite, called a strike. Then it waits nearby for the venom to work before swallowing the victim whole.

The cobra uses two long, sharp teeth at the front of its upper jaw to bite and inject its venom. These are called its fangs. The venom can kill most creatures.

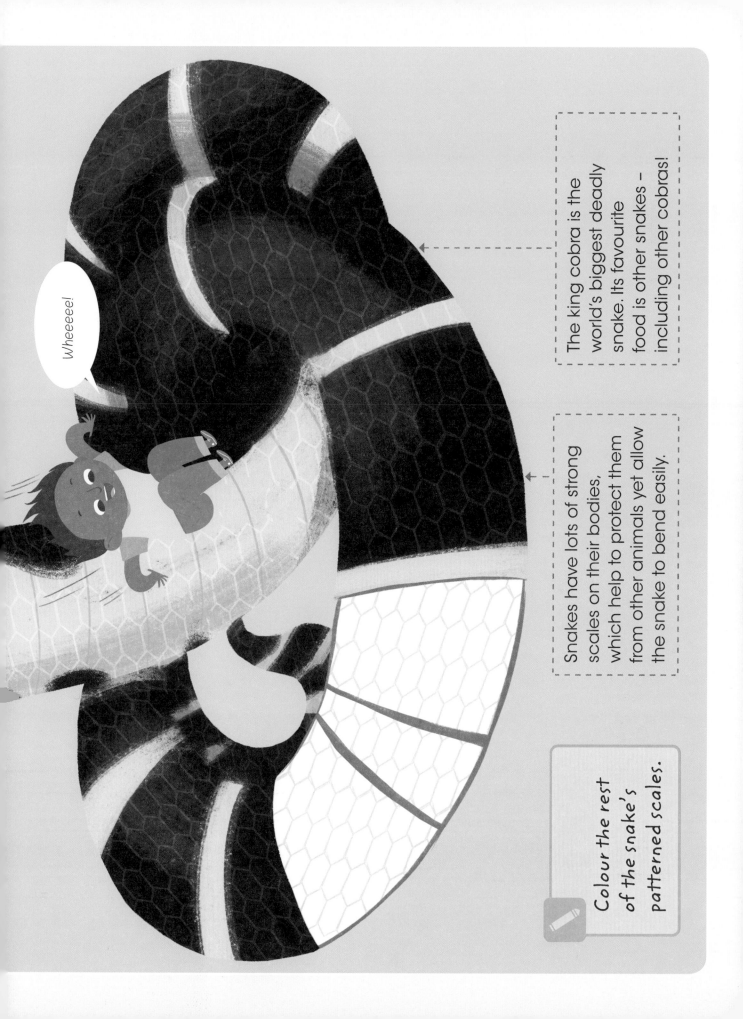

Wheeeee!

The king cobra is the world's biggest deadly snake. Its favourite food is other snakes – including other cobras!

Snakes have lots of strong scales on their bodies, which help to protect them from other animals yet allow the snake to bend easily.

Colour the rest of the snake's patterned scales.

Grasslands

Did you know that grasslands can be found on every continent, except Antarctica? They grow where there is not enough rain for trees, but too much rain for a desert.

In the dry season, there's no rain for months. So the grasses gradually turn brown!

Black-tailed jack rabbit

American bison

Prairie dogs

In **North America**, areas covered with grasses are known as **prairies**.

In the wet season, it rains hard, with thunder, lightning and storms. So fresh green grass can grow!

Giant anteater

Rhea

In **South America**, grasses can be twice as tall as you are! The name for grassland here is **pampas**.

Can you find these animals on the map? Write their names below.

Mongolian wild horse

Saker falcon

In **Central Asia**, dry grasslands cover vast, windy areas. They are known as **steppes**.

Giraffe

Emu

In **East Africa**, the flat grasslands are called **savannah**.

Hyena

In **Australia**, areas of spiky grasses and thorny shrubs are called **bush**.

Pretty-faced wallaby

Life on the move

Animals that eat mostly grass are called grazers. They are always on the move to find fresh green grass to eat.

A **leopard** waits for a young, old or sick animal to get left behind.

Home den

Wildebeest stamp, snort and grunt as they sniff the air for fresh grass.

The predators who hunt the grazers must stay on the move too!

Waterhole

Giraffes can see over other animals and keep a lookout for faraway danger.

African wild dogs rest and sleep in homes called dens.

Fresh grass

Zebras move their big ears to listen for sounds of predators.

Thomson's gazelles like to gather at pools to drink.

? Follow the lines to work out which animal is going where.

29

African elephant

ANIMAL FACT FILE

Animal group: Mammal

Height: 3.5 metres

Habitat: Grasslands, woodlands

Where in the world: Africa

Main foods: Grasses, leaves, fruits, bark

In danger?: Yes – vulnerable

The elephant's tail swishes away flies and other pests.

Join the dots to see who is following its mother.

An elephant can walk for days! Its long legs can take big steps.

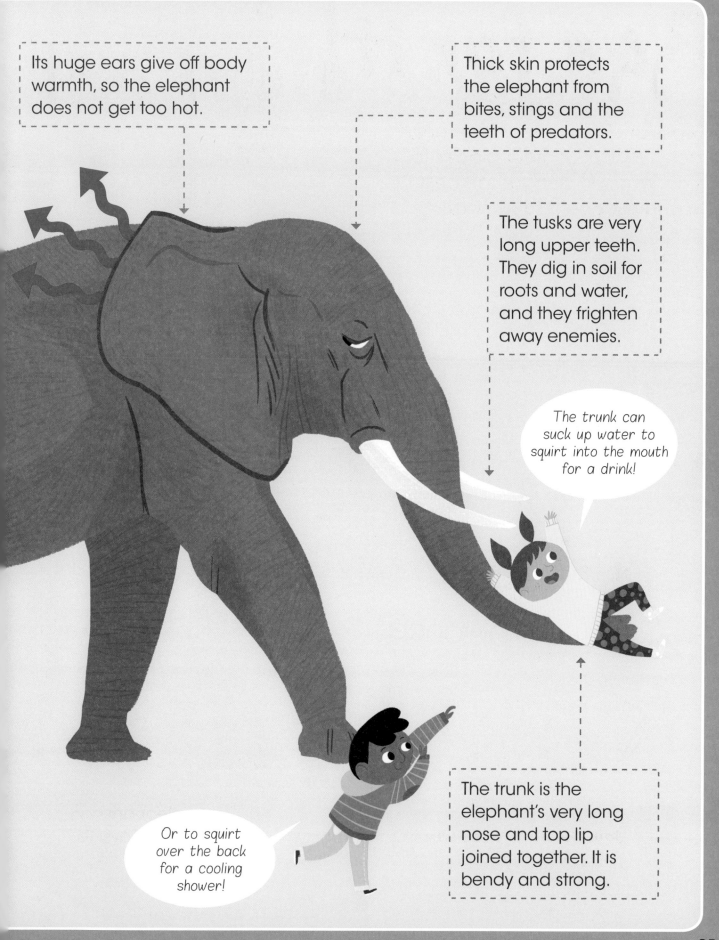

Its huge ears give off body warmth, so the elephant does not get too hot.

Thick skin protects the elephant from bites, stings and the teeth of predators.

The tusks are very long upper teeth. They dig in soil for roots and water, and they frighten away enemies.

The trunk can suck up water to squirt into the mouth for a drink!

Or to squirt over the back for a cooling shower!

The trunk is the elephant's very long nose and top lip joined together. It is bendy and strong.

Run for it!

Grasslands have very few trees, rocks, valleys or other places to hide. When in danger, the best way to escape is to run fast!

A kangaroo can leap a length of 5 metres in a single hop. Ask someone to measure that along the ground. Then see how far you and your friends can long-jump!

The **white rhino** of Africa can charge for a short distance at 50 kilometres per hour.

Name	Distance

The **grey kangaroo** of Australia can reach a top speed of 70 kilometres per hour. Each hop covers a great distance.

The **maned wolf** of South America can sprint at almost 60 kilometres per hour.

The **ostrich** of Africa is the world's fastest running bird. It can stride at 75 kilometres per hour.

The **pronghorn** of North America can speed at more than 85 kilometres per hour.

Turn the page to find out about the animal that beats the pronghorn!

Cheetah

ANIMAL FACT FILE

 Animal group: Mammal

 Length: 2.2 metres, including tail

 Habitat: Grasslands, scattered woodland, scrub

 Where in the world: Africa and South-West Asia

 Main foods: Animals, from mice to antelopes

 In danger?: Yes – vulnerable

It's too fast for me to photograph!

The cheetah can run at speeds of around 114 kilometres per hour, accelerating fast to chase down its prey.

Its tail helps a cheetah balance while it's running.

The cheetah's claws are partly out at all times to grip the ground, so it is always ready to run!

The two black lines on a cheetah's face are called 'tear marks'. Each line runs from the inside corner of the eye to the corner of the mouth. Finish the other side of the cheetah's face.

Don't worry! The cheetah can only keep its top speed for less than a minute.

The cheetah's body is perfectly shaped for speed. It has a super-flexible back that helps it take long, fast strides.

Grassland food

The main food in the grassland is... grass! So it's not surprising that most food chains here start with grass stems, leaves, seeds or roots.

AFRICA

The lion is the top meat-eater in this food chain. It hunts a plant-eater: the grant's gazelle. The gazelle eats grass leaves.

Lion

Grant's gazelle

SOUTH AMERICA

The jaguar is the top meat-eater here. It eats other meat-eaters, like the giant anteater, who eats termites. Termites are plant-eaters – they eat grass roots.

Jaguar

Giant anteater

ASIA

There are three meat-eaters in this food chain: the steppe eagle, steppe polecat and racerunner lizard. The darkling beetle is a plant-eater that eats grass seeds.

Steppe eagle

Steppe polecat

A food chain shows what each living thing eats!

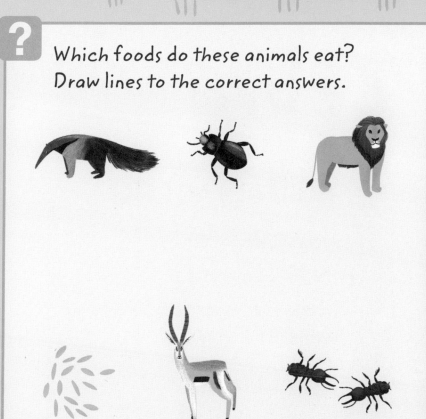

Which foods do these animals eat? Draw lines to the correct answers.

Grass leaves

Termites

Grass roots

Or who is eating whom!

Racerunner lizard

Darkling beetle

Grass seeds

Zebra

ANIMAL FACT FILE

 Animal group: Mammal

 Height: 2.2 metres

 Habitat: Grasslands, scrub and shrub

 Where in the world: East and southern Africa

 Main foods: Grasses, flowers, leaves

 In danger?: Not yet

The zebra has very good senses. Its large eyes see far, its big ears hear faint sounds and its long nose picks up many smells.

Its wide, strong teeth munch grasses for up to 16 hours each day.

No-one really knows why zebras have stripes! Some possible reasons are:

- Maybe for camouflage, to help it hide among tall grasses and bushes.
- Perhaps to recognize each other, since every zebra has a slightly different pattern.
- Possibly to stay cool.
- Maybe to make it difficult for a predator to pick out one zebra from a group.

Baby zebras, like baby horses, are called foals.

Foals can stand up, walk and run only one hour after being born!

Can you add the foal's stripes?

Polar regions

The polar regions are the coldest places on Earth. They are covered with ice and snow for much of the year. Despite this, wild animals manage to survive there!

Join the dots to see which white animal is riding on the iceberg.

Arctic

The **right whale** comes to the surface to breathe, before diving again to feed.

The **Northern fulmar** plunges into the water to catch shrimps, fish and squid.

The **hooded seal** is a speedy swimmer. It chases smaller creatures for food.

North Pole (Arctic)

The Arctic is an ocean. Huge floating sheets of ice and lumps of ice, called icebergs, float across it.

South Pole (Antarctic)

The Antarctic is a huge area of land, covered with ice.

Antarctic

Wow! It's almost as big as a REAL elephant!

The **South polar skua** flies over the ice, looking for dead fish and other scraps of food.

The **Southern elephant seal** dives deep to catch fish and squid.

Chinstrap penguins gather together on an iceberg to rest.

Keeping warm

When it's cold outside, we wrap up warm!
But how do polar animals keep the heat
in and the cold out?

Brr! In polar regions, it's cold all year round!

GYRFALCON

The gyrfalcon is a big Arctic bird of prey. Its tough outer feathers keep out the worst weather. Beneath the outer feathers are soft, fluffy feathers, called down, to keep in its body warmth.

Feathers overlap to keep out wind

BELUGA WHALE

The beluga is a 5-metre-long Arctic whale. Under its white skin is a thick layer of fat, called blubber. The blubber works like an all-over sleeping bag, keeping the beluga warm.

ARCTIC FOX

The Arctic fox's thick fur keeps out wind, rain, sleet and snow. It wraps its tail around itself like a cosy scarf. Even if it sleeps in the open, covered with snow, it stays warm.

Outer layer of skin

Inner layer of skin

Layer of blubber up to 10 cm thick

Connective tissue

Fibrous tissue

Muscle

Try this insulation experiment!

1

Take two ice cubes the same size and put each one on a plate.

2

Wrap one ice cube in material, such as a towel. Or put it in an old woolly sock or glove.

3

Put both plates in a warm place. You should discover that the ice cube that is not wrapped melts first. Why?

Polar bear

I'd better watch out! Polar bears are the world's largest meat-eaters on land!

ANIMAL FACT FILE

 Animal group: Mammal

 Height: 3 metres, standing on back legs

 Habitat: Ocean, icebergs, coasts

 Where in the world: All around the Arctic

 Main foods: Seals, crabs, seabirds, fish, whales

 In danger?: Yes – vulnerable

A polar bear's paws have hairy soles, to grip slippery ice.

Its big, sharp claws work like hooks to catch seals and other prey.

The outer layer of guard hair is long and strong. The inner layer of underfur is soft and warm.

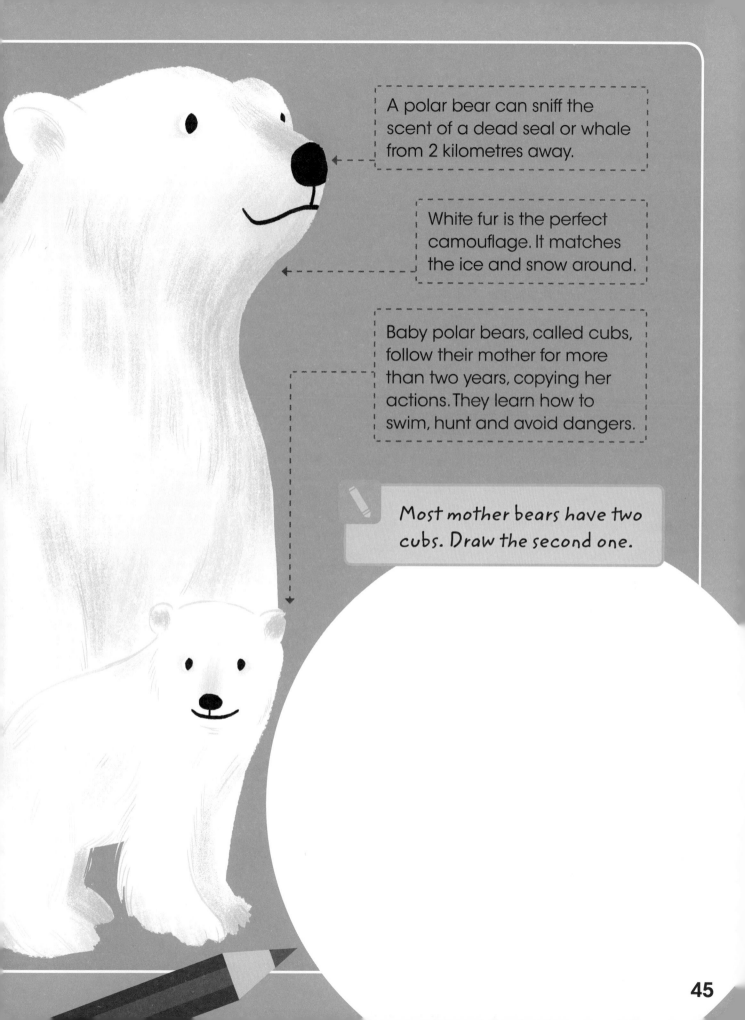

A polar bear can sniff the scent of a dead seal or whale from 2 kilometres away.

White fur is the perfect camouflage. It matches the ice and snow around.

Baby polar bears, called cubs, follow their mother for more than two years, copying her actions. They learn how to swim, hunt and avoid dangers.

Most mother bears have two cubs. Draw the second one.

Speedy swimmers

Seals, fur seals and walruses all have strong flippers for fast swimming. They belong to the animal group called pinnipeds.

The **harp seal** lives in the Arctic Ocean.

The **walrus** lives in the Arctic Ocean.

Front and rear flippers can waddle on land

? **True or false?** Tick the boxes.

	TRUE	FALSE
The walrus lives in the Antarctic.		
The fur seal has very little fur.		
The harp seal has sharp teeth.		
The walrus's long teeth are called fangs.		

The **Northern fur seal** lives in the north Pacific Ocean.

Fur seals make loud barks like a dog!

Swims with whole body and rear flipper

Fur with back patch shaped like a harp (musical instrument)

Rear flippers are useless on land

Medium-sized sharp teeth to catch small prey

Pinky-brown skin with very little fur

Very long upper teeth called tusks

Swims with front flippers

Front and rear flippers can waddle on land

Very thick brown fur

Swims with front flippers

Large dog-like teeth to catch big prey

Emperor penguin

The emperor weighs up to 50 kilograms – probably more than you!

ANIMAL FACT FILE

Animal group: Bird

Height: 1.2 metres

Habitat: Icy places such as icebergs and frozen shores

Where in the world: Antarctica

Main foods: Fish, shellfish, squid

In danger?: Not quite – near threatened

Its body is smooth and streamlined for fast swimming.

The emperor penguin has a thick, fatty layer, called blubber, under its skin to keep it warm.

The penguin's feathers are strong and waterproof.

Its wings are small and useless for flying. But they are fantastic swimming flippers.

The penguin spends much time preening – cleaning its feathers with its beak and feet.

Its wide feet grip ice well and stop the penguin from sinking in the snow.

Emperor penguins lay their eggs in the middle of winter. Each male balances an egg on his feet, covering it with a flap of belly skin so it does not freeze. The males gather together to keep warm. Help this dad get to the others at their nesting site.

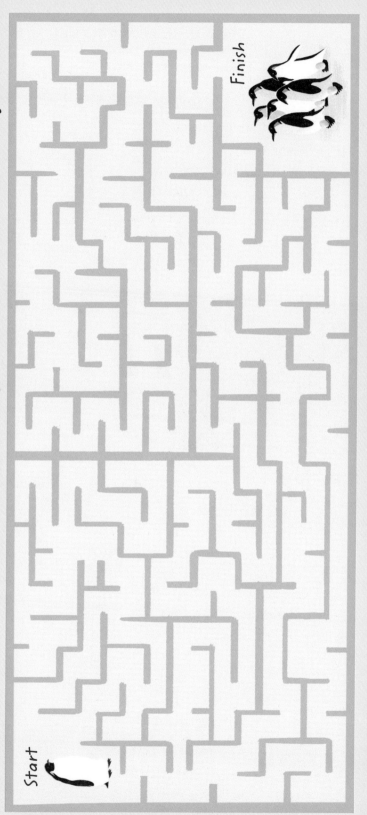

Start

Finish

Food in the sea

In polar regions, few plants grow on land, so most food chains start in the sea!

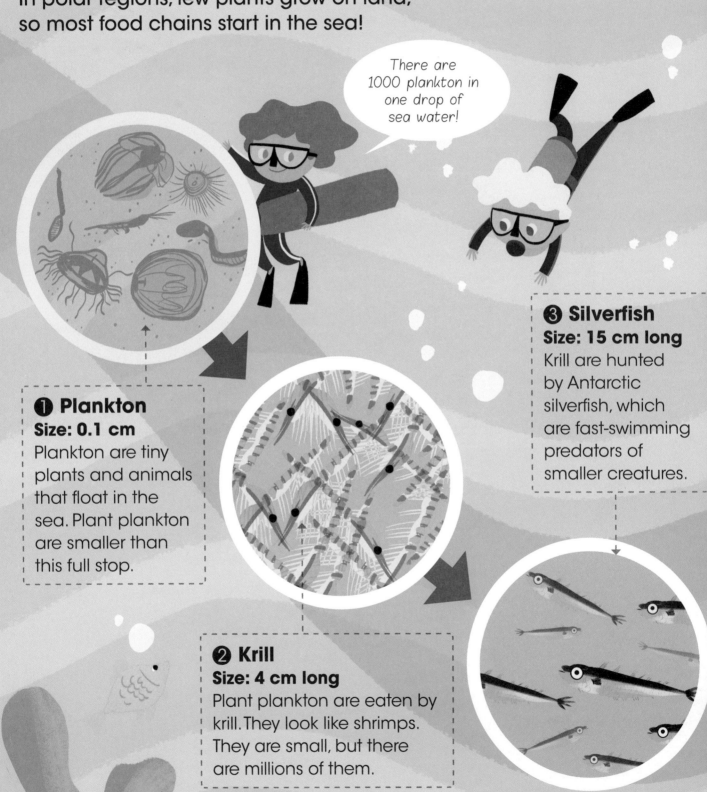

There are 1000 plankton in one drop of sea water!

❶ Plankton
Size: 0.1 cm
Plankton are tiny plants and animals that float in the sea. Plant plankton are smaller than this full stop.

❷ Krill
Size: 4 cm long
Plant plankton are eaten by krill. They look like shrimps. They are small, but there are millions of them.

❸ Silverfish
Size: 15 cm long
Krill are hunted by Antarctic silverfish, which are fast-swimming predators of smaller creatures.

❹ King penguin
Size: 100 cm tall
Silverfish are victims of the king penguin, which is the second largest of all the penguins.

❺ Leopard seal
Size: 300 cm long
Penguins are common prey of the leopard seal – a slim, strong, fast and fierce hunter.

❻ Killer whale
Size: 900 cm long
Even the leopard seal is not safe from one of the ocean's most fearsome predators, the killer whale.

Krill swim in crowded groups called shoals. How many krill are jumbled up here?

Deserts

Do you think all deserts are hot? Some are, but others are extremely cold! Some deserts are covered with sand, others are full of rocks. But all deserts are very, very dry.

Daytime
Most animals hide in their burrows to keep out of the sun. Some creatures wander around and look for food, although they try to stay in the shade.

The **secretary bird** walks long distances every day as it looks for its favourite foods: snakes, lizards, mice, rats and baby birds.

The **sandfish** is not a fish, but a kind of lizard. It wriggles through the loose sand hunting insects.

Yikes! The Sahara is the largest hot desert.

🔍 The Saharan silver ant comes out of its nest during the hottest part of the day to avoid predators. Can you find five ants before they return to their nests?

Night-time
Animals come out of their resting places to feed. It is much cooler, and the sand and rocks do not burn their feet.

The **eagle owl** looks and listens, before swooping silently onto small animals such as lizards, snakes, scorpions, mice and jerboas.

The **jerboa** has huge ears, a long tail and very long back legs for hopping about.

The **fat-tail scorpion** searches for prey such as insects and worms. It has powerful pincers and a deadly sting at the end of its tail.

The **darkling beetle** wanders through the sand and rocks to find seeds and plants to eat.

Finding water

I wouldn't need my umbrella in a desert!

In deserts, it hardly ever rains. The ground is dry for months, or even years, at a time. Only very tough plants can grow. So how do the animals survive?

ARABIAN ORYX

In African deserts, the Arabian oryx gets all its water from the plants it eats. It also saves water in its body by hardly ever peeing.

SPADEFOOT TOAD

In the deserts of south-west North America, the spadefoot toad digs down into loose, damp soil and waits until the rain returns.

BUDGERIGARS

In Australian deserts, small parrots called budgerigars fly long distances to waterholes. They form large flocks and stand around the water's edge to drink.

GERBIL

In Asian deserts, the gerbil stays in its burrow by day. It even blocks up the entrance with a stone or soil to keep in the moisture from its breath.

VISCACHAS

In South American deserts, viscachas live in underground burrows and tunnels. They dig deep to where the soil is damp, and lick water from the tunnel walls.

Try this water loss experiment!

❶ On a hot, sunny morning, cut out animal shapes from blotting paper and soak both of them in water.

❷ Put one animal where it will be in the sun all day. Put the other in a cool, shady place.

❸ After a few minutes, look at the animals. The one in the sun should have lost more water. This is why desert animals like to stay in the shade.

Ostrich

It uses its big, strong beak to peck and eat almost any food, from soft plants and worms to hard seeds and beetles.

The ostrich has the largest eye size of any land animal.

The ostrich is taller than a person. It can see a long way across the desert to look for food, and also to spot danger.

The ostrich is the world's largest bird!

The ostrich lays the largest eggs, each as big as 25 hens' eggs!

The ostrich's wings are too small for it to fly. But they can be waved like fans to keep the ostrich cool in the midday heat.

ANIMAL FACT FILE

 Animal group: Bird

 Height: 2.5 metres

 Habitat: Deserts, grasslands

 Where in the world: Africa

 Main foods: Almost anything, from buds to beetles

 In danger?: Not yet

The huge feet, with large toes, grip hard ground well.

Long legs allow the ostrich to run extremely fast. It can reach speeds of more than 70 kilometres per hour – almost twice as fast as a champion human sprinter.

Fill in the missing heights of some other big birds that cannot fly.

2 m

1.5 m

1 m

0.5 m

0 m

Name:	Rhea	Cassowary	Emu
Location:	South America	Australia	Australia
Height:	.... metres	.... metres	.... metres

Desert food

Desert food chains often include lizards and snakes. These reptiles, with their tough scales, need little water and survive well even in the driest places.

Nest

Rock

❶ Welwitschia
The Namib Desert of Africa is home to a strange plant called the welwitschia. Its leaves can grow up to 5 metres long.

❷ Termites
These ant-like insects live in tall mounds, called nests, made from sun-baked earth. Termites search for and eat small bits of plants.

❸ Barking gecko
This small lizard is hardly larger than your finger. It feeds mainly on termites, eating dozens each day.

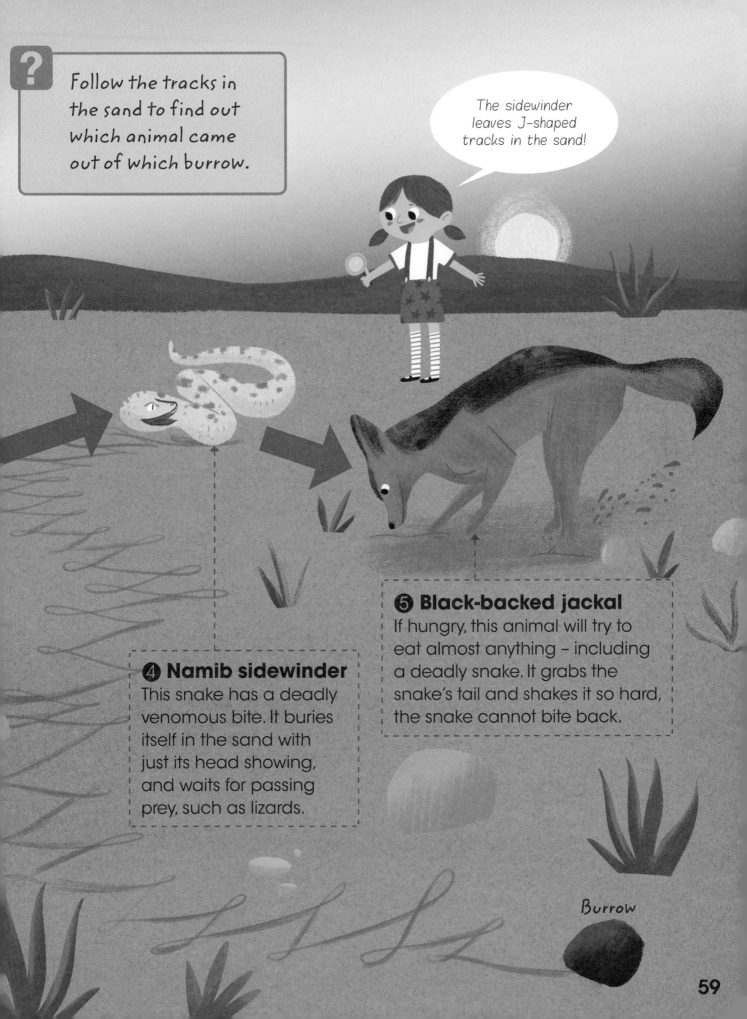

? Follow the tracks in the sand to find out which animal came out of which burrow.

The sidewinder leaves J-shaped tracks in the sand!

④ **Namib sidewinder**
This snake has a deadly venomous bite. It buries itself in the sand with just its head showing, and waits for passing prey, such as lizards.

⑤ **Black-backed jackal**
If hungry, this animal will try to eat almost anything – including a deadly snake. It grabs the snake's tail and shakes it so hard, the snake cannot bite back.

Burrow

Camel

A camel can drink 200 litres of water in 3 minutes!

ANIMAL FACT FILE

 Animal group: Mammal

 Height: 2 metres

 Habitat: Deserts, grasslands, scrub

 Main foods: Plants

 In danger?: Bactrian – yes, dromedary – not yet

Dromedary camel

Long eyelashes help to keep sand and dust out of the camel's eyes.

The one-humped camel, or dromedary, is found in hot and sandy deserts in Africa and the Middle East.

Wide, padded feet stop the dromedary camel from sinking into the soft desert sand.

Its tough mouth can chew all kinds of desert plants, even those with thorns and spines.

The dromedary camel has a short coat of fur.

Bactrian camel

Its humps are mainly fat!

The two-humped, or bactrian, camel is from cold and mostly rocky deserts in Asia.

A camel's body temperature can rise by several degrees without making it sweat, which saves water.

The bactrian camel has a thick, shaggy coat in winter that it sheds when temperatures rise.

Its nostrils can close to keep out sand and dust.

The bactrian camel has hard, tough feet that can withstand stones and rocks.

Do you know your camels? Tick the boxes to match the correct type of camel to the descriptions.

	Dromedary	Bactrian
I have one hump.	☐	☐
My fur is long and shaggy.	☐	☐
My feet are wide and padded.	☐	☐
I live in cold, mostly rocky deserts.	☐	☐

Super-senses

Desert animals have amazing senses that help them to find food and avoid dangers.

Hyper-hearing!

The **fennec fox** has huge ears to hear the tiny sounds of its prey, including mice, beetles and ants.

The **desert golden mole** uses its long whiskers and thick fur to pick up movements of worms or insects nearby.

Mega motion detection!

Smells by tasting!

The **desert death adder** flicks out its tongue to collect tiny smells floating in the air. Then it tastes the smell in its mouth.

Heat sense!

The **Mongolian pit viper** has holes, called pits, between its eyes and nostrils. The pits detect heat from animals, so the snake can find its prey in darkness.

The **spotted hyena's** large nose follows the scents of antelopes, gazelles and other creatures. It can also smell a dead animal from kilometres away.

Super-smell!

A hyena's sense of smell is 100 times better than mine!

Join the dots to find another desert animal with super-hearing!

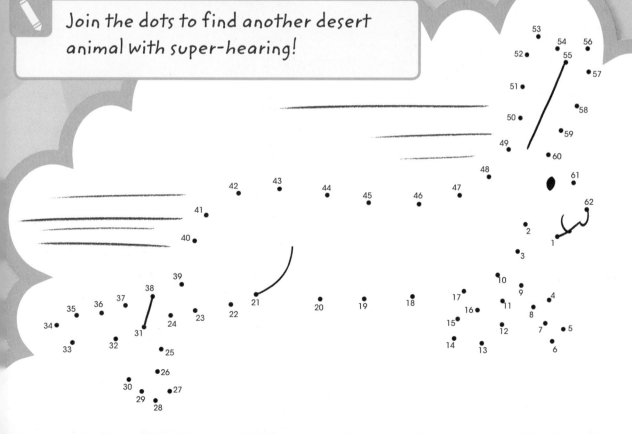

Temperate woods

Temperate woodlands are always busy with life! They have warm summers, cool winters and steady amounts of rain throughout the year.

Spring

It is warm and bright. Tree leaves grow, and flowers cover the woodland floor. Many animals become more active. They feed hungrily.

The leaves are wide and flat.

The **jay** gets ready to make a nest and raise a family.

The **red fox** mother stays in her den (burrow) with her new babies, called kits. The father brings food.

The **peacock butterfly** has woken up after her winter sleep. She lays her eggs on nettles.

The **tawny owl's** chicks have grown up and left.

Autumn
It is cool and gloomy. Tree leaves turn yellow and brown, and fall from the branches. Some animals leave, others prepare for winter.

The **wild boar** grows fat on the plentiful fruits, berries, spiders and worms.

The slow-worm is not actually a worm, or a snake. It is a lizard without legs!

The **slow-worm** burrows into the soil or under a rock for winter.

65

Tree feasts

In a woodland, the trees provide most food. So the food chains start with buds, flowers, leaves, fruits, roots, shoots, bark – even solid wood!

The **wildcat** hunts many creatures, including mice, squirrels, birds, and even the weasel.

Wood pigeons peck apart and swallow acorns as fast as they can.

Squirrels eat some acorns and bury others to eat later.

The **great tit** feeds on acorns, including any bugs in them.

The **acorn moth grub** munches its way into an acorn.

The **sparrowhawk** preys on small woodland birds.

The **weasel** hunts mice, voles and similar small mammals.

Deathwatch beetle grubs chew the wood, making tunnels deep into the tree.

Wood mice nibble acorns when they fall to the ground.

Wow! Just one oak tree can be home and food for more than 400 creatures!

Go wild with this wildcat mask!

① With the help of an adult, cut a cat's face from a paper plate or piece of card. Colour it in.

② Make holes for the whiskers. Poke drinking straws through the holes, and glue them in place on the inside.

③ Make two holes, one on each side. Tie a piece of elastic through the holes. Now wear your mask and be a top cat!

Moose

Male moose shed their antlers in winter to save energy. A new set regrows in spring.

This hump stores extra energy in the form of fat.

At breeding time, male moose make a bellowing noise!

It's so loud that it can be heard 3 kilometres away!

Moose have no upper front teeth. But the tough top lip and sharp lower front teeth easily bite plant foods.

Under the moose's chin is a flap of skin and fur, called a dewlap.

ANIMAL FACT FILE

 Animal group: Mammal

 Height: 2 metres

 Habitat: Woodlands, forests

 Where in the world: North America, Europe, North Asia

 Main foods: Leaves, twigs, buds, fruits

 In danger?: Not yet

In North America, this deer is called a moose. In Europe, it is an elk or alg, and in East Asia, a tuolu!

Here is a male moose in winter. Draw him as he looks in summer!

A moose's legs are long, and its hooves are sharp. It kicks fast and hard.

Life underground

Holes, burrows and tunnels are made by many woodland creatures. Some burrowers are as small as earthworms, others as big as badgers.

Badgers live in a network of burrows called a sett.

Earthworms eat their way through soil, taking in tiny bits of food.

B

The male badger is called a boar, the female is a sow and the youngsters are cubs.

The nest chamber is at the end of a tunnel.

C

71

Giant panda

ANIMAL FACT FILE

 Animal group: Mammal

 Length: 1.5 metres long

 Habitat: Bamboo woods

 Where in the world: East Asia

 Main foods: Bamboos

 In danger?: Yes – endangered

A panda's paw has five clawed fingers, plus an extra bone that works like a thumb.

The giant panda has long, sharp teeth suited to eating meat, yet it mostly eats plants!

The giant panda eats bamboo, which is a kind of grass that grows as tall as trees.

A panda spends most of its day chewing bamboo leaves and stems.

A mother panda has one cub at a time. It is tiny when born – smaller than your fist!

Did you know that there are probably fewer than 3000 wild giant pandas left?

Giant pandas sometimes eat other foods, such as fish, frogs and eggs.

Colour the shapes to match the coloured dots to reveal a little cub.

Deep sleep

Winter in woodlands is cold, dull and rainy. One way to survive is just to sleep right through it! This is called hibernation.

In New Zealand, when it is very cold, the **short-tailed bat** sleeps in a tree hole or cave.

In Europe, the **hedgehog** makes a nest under a woodland bush or log.

In Australia, the **striped burrowing frog** digs down into the woodland soil and stays there.

ZZZZZZZz

Sometimes a hibernating hedgehog is joined by some friends!

If the sun shines, the bats may wake up for a day or two!

In North America, the **black bear** hibernates in its den. Its heartbeat and breathing slow down and its body becomes cold.

In Europe, the **dormouse** makes a nest of grass, leaves, moss, feathers and fur among plants and roots.

zzzzZZZZZZZ

True or false? Tick the boxes.

TRUE FALSE

The short-tailed bat does not wake up during its hibernation.

The black bear's heartbeat slows down when it hibernates.

Hedgehogs only ever hibernate in pairs or groups.

Imagine staying asleep for months at a time!

Rivers and lakes

Freshwater habitats can vary from speedy streams to wide rivers, from little ponds to vast lakes, and from cold marshes to tropical swamps!

Look! The river starts as a few shallow streams, flowing into one.

Yes, and as more streams join, the river gets wider!

The **water vole** lives in a burrow in the river bank. It eats leaves, grass, waterweeds and other plants.

The **kingfisher** sits on a branch above the river, watching for fish. Then it dives like an arrow into the water to catch its meal.

The **dipper** walks along the stream bed, as it pecks among the pebbles for worms and bugs.

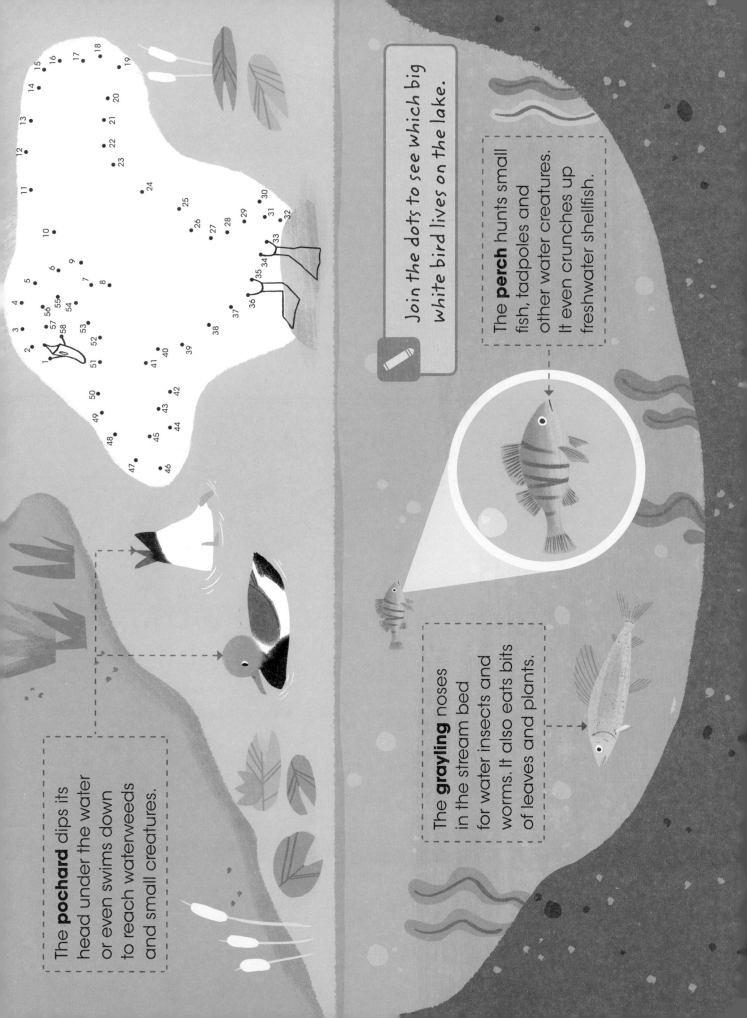

Join the dots to see which big white bird lives on the lake.

The **perch** hunts small fish, tadpoles and other water creatures. It even crunches up freshwater shellfish.

The **grayling** noses in the stream bed for water insects and worms. It also eats bits of leaves and plants.

The **pochard** dips its head under the water or even swims down to reach waterweeds and small creatures.

Super-swimmers

Moving in water uses more energy and muscle power than moving on land. So most creatures have streamlined bodies that slip easily through the water, and fins, flippers or webbed feet to push themselves along.

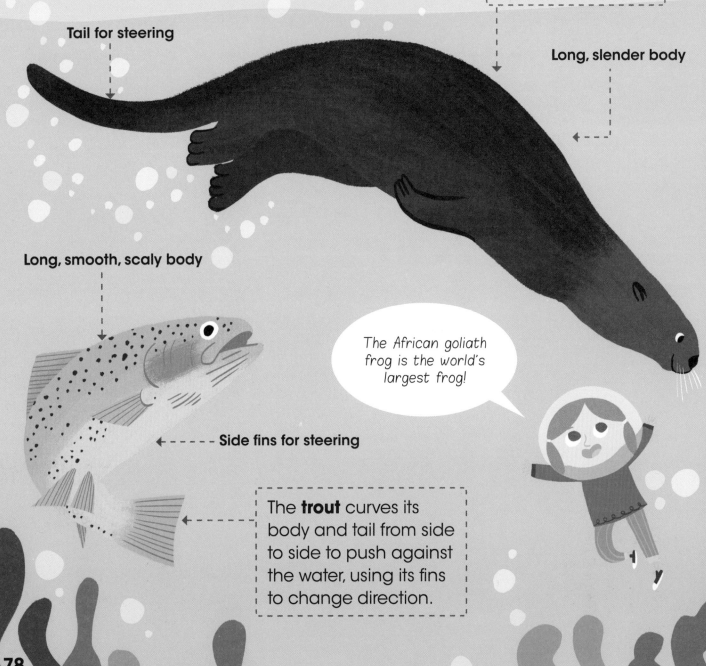

The **otter** has flaps of skin between its toes (webs). It chases fish, frogs and other prey.

Tail for steering

Long, slender body

Long, smooth, scaly body

The African goliath frog is the world's largest frog!

Side fins for steering

The **trout** curves its body and tail from side to side to push against the water, using its fins to change direction.

Long, sharp beak

The **black-throated diver** kicks its webbed feet and flaps its wings as it swims after fish and frogs.

Small paddle-like wings

Large webbed feet

I'll take a photograph!

Powerful back legs

Webs

The **African goliath frog** swims by kicking its huge, strong back feet, with long toes joined by webs.

 Try this paddle power experiment!

1

Part-fill a bowl, basin or sink with water. Move your hand through the water, fingers spread. Feel how much water you can push.

2

Put your hand in a small plastic bag and do the same.

3

Feel how much more water you push. That's why webbed feet are good for swimming fast.

Hippopotamus

ANIMAL FACT FILE

 Animal group: Mammal

 Length: 4 metres

 Habitat: Rivers and lakes

 Where in the world: Central and southern Africa

 Main foods: Grass and water plants

 In danger?: Yes – vulnerable

Most mammals have fur or hair. But the hippo has almost none, apart from whiskers on the snout.

The hippo has huge, tusk-like canine teeth. It uses them for fighting to be boss of the herd, and for defence against predators.

The hippo uses its wide, bendy lips to pull up plants such as grasses, which it then chews with its cheek teeth.

Hippos are the third-largest land animals, after elephants and rhinos.

Hippos can walk and swim underwater. They close their nostrils and can hold their breath for more than 5 minutes.

Why do you think hippos wallow in mud?
- Maybe to keep their skin from drying out.
- Possibly to create a kind of sunscreen.
- Perhaps to keep cool.
- The real reason could be all these answers.

Add mud splats on the baby hippo!

The hippo can run at 30 kilometres per hour, which is faster than many humans.

Little and large

Some freshwater fish are as long as a car, others are smaller than your fingertip. Take a look at a few of the most interesting!

Piranha
Size: 25 cm long
Piranhas live in shoals (groups) and have a fierce bite, so they can attack animals much larger than themselves.

Common eel
Size: 100 cm long
The common eel has two small front fins, and one long fin that goes along its back and around its tail to the underside.

Large, blade-like, razor-sharp teeth

The eel's snake-like body has very tiny scales

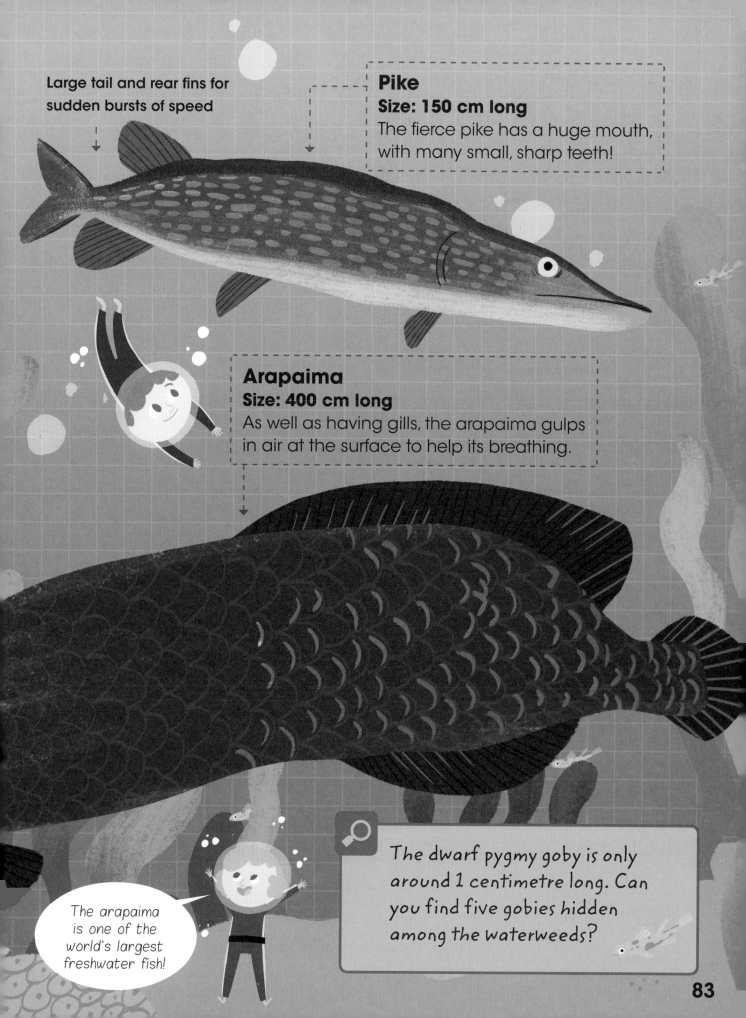

Large tail and rear fins for sudden bursts of speed

Pike
Size: 150 cm long
The fierce pike has a huge mouth, with many small, sharp teeth!

Arapaima
Size: 400 cm long
As well as having gills, the arapaima gulps in air at the surface to help its breathing.

The dwarf pygmy goby is only around 1 centimetre long. Can you find five gobies hidden among the waterweeds?

The arapaima is one of the world's largest freshwater fish!

Nile crocodile

ANIMAL FACT FILE

 Animal group: Reptile

Length: 1.5 metres

Habitat: Rivers, lakes, swamps

Where in the world: Africa

Main foods: All kinds of animals, from fish to zebras

In danger?: Not yet

The crocodile has thick skin and scales. Only lions, leopards and hyenas can bite through these.

The crocodile's eyes, ears and nostrils are on the top of its head, so it can float low in the water, yet still see, hear and breathe.

It has 60 to 70 pointed teeth in its long jaws!

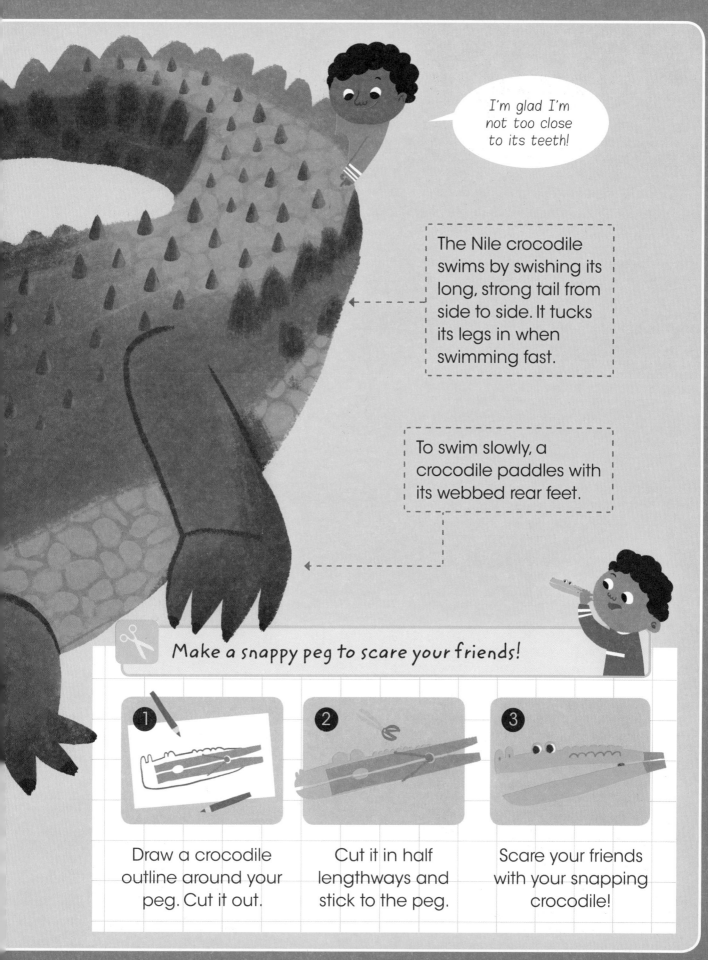

I'm glad I'm not too close to its teeth!

The Nile crocodile swims by swishing its long, strong tail from side to side. It tucks its legs in when swimming fast.

To swim slowly, a crocodile paddles with its webbed rear feet.

Make a snappy peg to scare your friends!

1. Draw a crocodile outline around your peg. Cut it out.

2. Cut it in half lengthways and stick to the peg.

3. Scare your friends with your snapping crocodile!

Changing shape

Some creatures live in water when young. Then, as they grow up, they change shape and start living on land or up in the air!

A dragonfly lays over 1500 eggs!

❶ Eggs
A dragonfly begins life as a tiny egg – on, in or under the leaf of a water plant.

❷ Young nymph
The egg hatches into a nymph. It has gills, six legs and a big, strong mouth.

Dragonfly life cycle

❹ Adult dragonfly
The skin splits for the last time, and out comes the four-winged adult dragonfly. It is a swift hunter of flies, gnats and similar creatures.

❸ Nymph
The nymph sheds its skin and grows a new, bigger one. It does this several times over two or three years, then crawls up a reed stem into the air.

❶ Frogspawn
A frog begins life as a jelly-covered egg in a big lump of eggs called frogspawn.

❷ Young tadpole
The egg hatches into a tadpole. It has gills, a big head and a wriggly tail.

Frog
life cycle

❹ Adult frog
It is now a grown-up frog that can live in water or on land. It feeds on all kinds of worms, bugs and insects.

❸ Tadpole
The tadpole grows back legs, then front legs. Its gills and tail shrink. It develops lungs to breathe air.

The change in body shape is known as metamorphosis.

Colour the frog to complete the transformation!

Conifer trees

Conifer forest trees include pines, firs and spruces.

Conifer forests have a short, warm summer and a long, snowy winter. Some of the world's fiercest animals live here.

Summer

In summer, the **elk** munches on buds and shoots.

The **sable** hunts mice, rats, voles, lemmings and other small prey.

The **capercaillie** feeds on the ground, eating bugs, worms and shoots.

The **taiga vole** chomps on most kinds of plant foods in summer.

Help these animals find their way through the trees to their favourite winter foods.

Winter

 In winter, the **elk** searches for mosses and ferns to eat. It scrapes away snow with its hooves.

 The **sable** comes out of its winter burrow now and then to hunt small animals.

 The **capercaillie** feeds in the trees, pecking conifer leaves, buds and seeds.

 The **taiga vole** eats grass, horsetails and other plants.

Beaver lodge

Beavers build a winter home, called a lodge. Even when ice covers their pool, they can swim out, gather their stored food and take it back to eat!

Beavers make a pool by building a dam across the stream.

The lodge is very strong and has an underwater entrance to keep out predators, such as wolves and lynx.

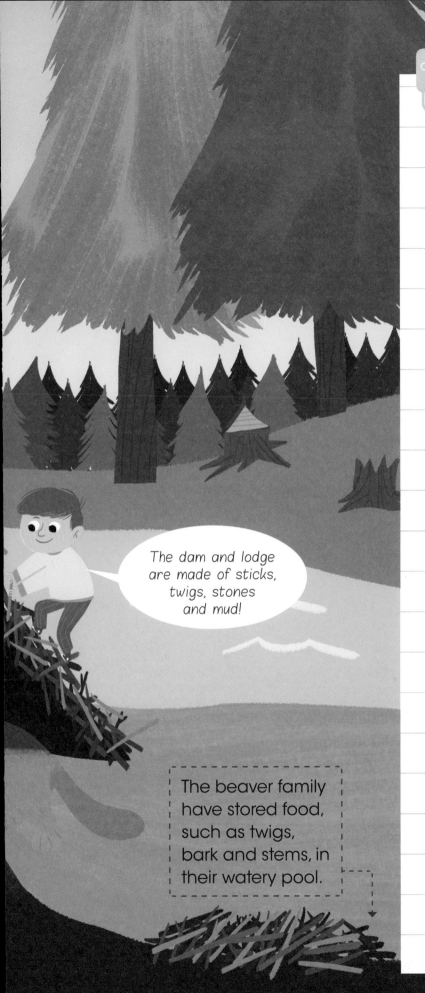

The dam and lodge are made of sticks, twigs, stones and mud!

The beaver family have stored food, such as twigs, bark and stems, in their watery pool.

Build a beaver lodge!

1 Gather your supplies: long, thin items like drinking straws, lollipop sticks and cocktail sticks, plus tissue paper.

2 First, bend some straws into a C-shaped framework. Then weave the other items in and out. Use wet tissue paper to hold everything in place. Put this on a sheet of blue card.

3 Shape some beavers from brown modelling clay. Don't forget the wide, flat tail!

Siberian tiger

ANIMAL FACT FILE

 Animal group: Mammal

 Length: 3 metres, including tail

 Habitat: Conifer forests, mountains

 Where in the world: East Asia

 Main foods: Deer, boar, rabbits, other mammals

 In danger?: Yes – endangered

The Siberian tiger is the world's largest big cat. Males weigh over 200 kilograms, and females up to 150 kilograms.

Tigers use their long front teeth, called canines, to kill their prey.

The tiger's whiskers help it to feel its way at night, when it hunts.

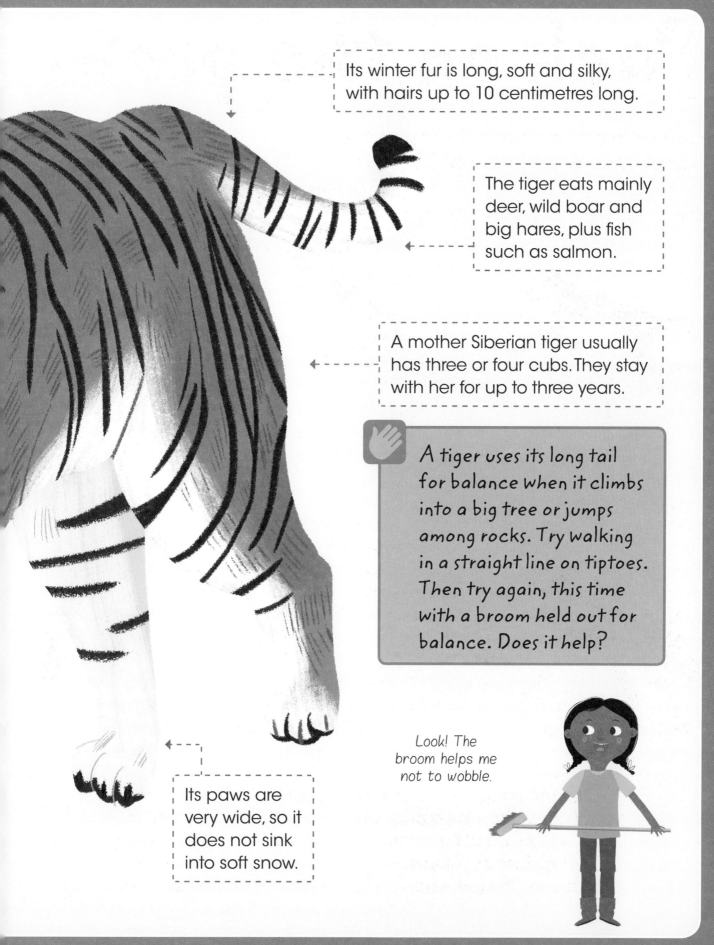

Its winter fur is long, soft and silky, with hairs up to 10 centimetres long.

The tiger eats mainly deer, wild boar and big hares, plus fish such as salmon.

A mother Siberian tiger usually has three or four cubs. They stay with her for up to three years.

A tiger uses its long tail for balance when it climbs into a big tree or jumps among rocks. Try walking in a straight line on tiptoes. Then try again, this time with a broom held out for balance. Does it help?

Look! The broom helps me not to wobble.

Its paws are very wide, so it does not sink into soft snow.

Pack on the prowl

Conifer forests are home to one of the world's most widespread and feared predators – the grey wolf. Most grey wolves live in family groups called packs.

1 Members of the pack hunt together. The main hunters are the chief adults, called the alpha male and alpha female.

2 The wolves prey on the old, young, injured or sick. They surround the victim, then dash in, biting it around the rear end.

3 The alpha pair eats first. The others wait their turn, before feeding on what is left: often just skin, gristle and bones.

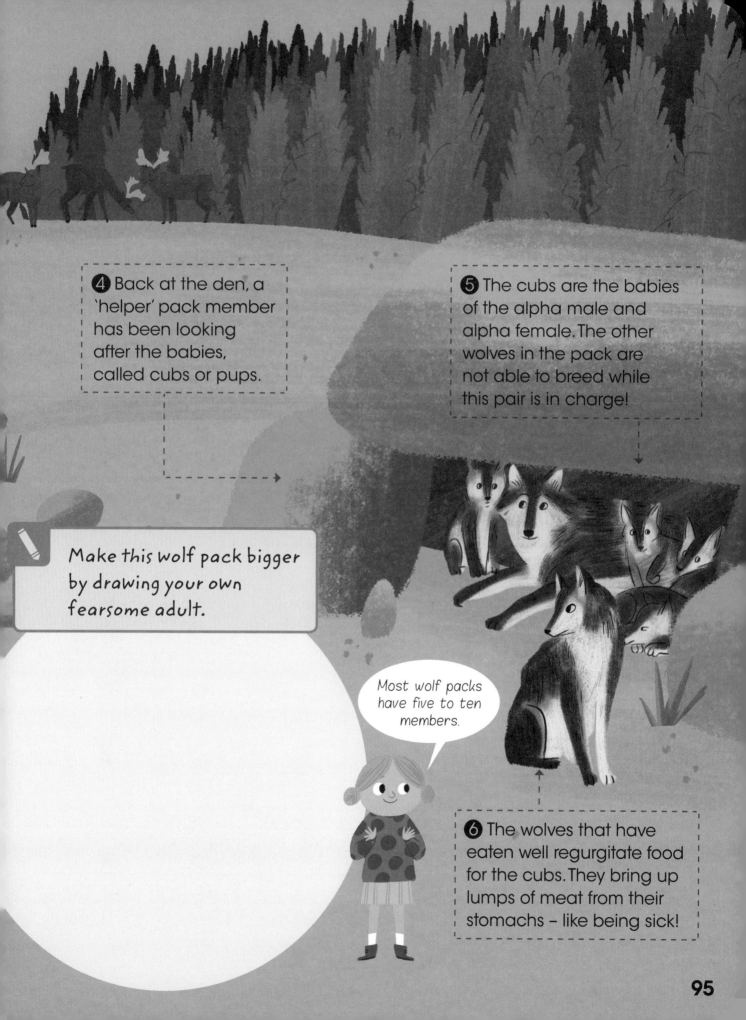

④ Back at the den, a 'helper' pack member has been looking after the babies, called cubs or pups.

⑤ The cubs are the babies of the alpha male and alpha female. The other wolves in the pack are not able to breed while this pair is in charge!

Make this wolf pack bigger by drawing your own fearsome adult.

Most wolf packs have five to ten members.

⑥ The wolves that have eaten well regurgitate food for the cubs. They bring up lumps of meat from their stomachs – like being sick!

Grizzly bear

The grizzly bear is a large kind of brown bear. It has pale tips to its hairs, making it look old or 'grizzled'.

It often stands on its back legs to get a better view, smell the air, and find food or detect danger.

ANIMAL FACT FILE

 Animal group: Mammal

 Height: 3 metres, standing

 Habitat: Forests, woods, mountains

 Where in the world: North America

 Main foods: Almost anything

 In danger?: Not yet

Grizzly bears feed hungrily in autumn. They store the extra energy as body fat.

The long, curved claws can swipe and scoop salmon and other fish from the water.

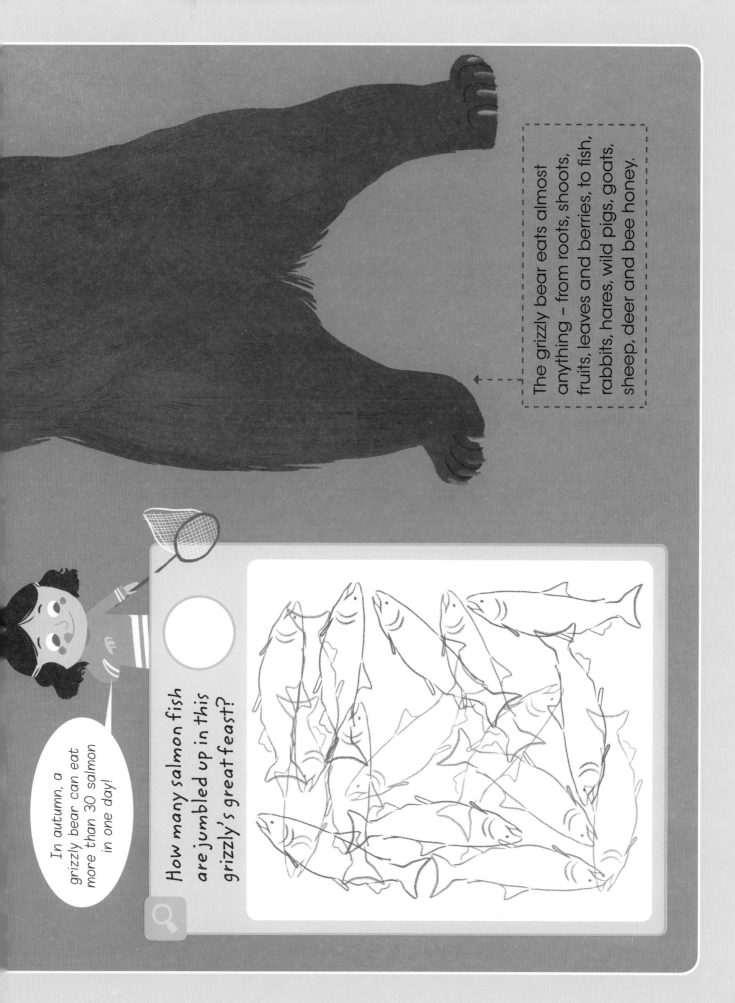

The grizzly bear eats almost anything – from roots, shoots, fruits, leaves and berries, to fish, rabbits, hares, wild pigs, goats, sheep, deer and bee honey.

In autumn, a grizzly bear can eat more than 30 salmon in one day!

How many salmon fish are jumbled up in this grizzly's great feast?

Fly in, fly out

Winter is so long and cold in conifer forests that many birds leave. Each year, they arrive in spring, feed and raise their young in summer and leave in autumn!

Summer visits can be very short.

Spring

The **Siberian thrush** flies in from warmer southern areas.

The **bean goose** usually lands in the same area each year. It looks for its old nesting site near water.

The **yellow warbler** reaches the conifer forest in April or May.

Summer

The Siberian thrush makes its nest in a bush or small tree.

The bean goose nest is a small scrape or hollow under a shrub or bush.

Grab a piece of paper and make your own flying bird!

Launch your bird and see how far it flies!

1 Fold top corners into the centre line. Then fold in again.

2 Fold in half lengthways. Fold down to make wings.

3 Draw on the bird's beak, eyes and feathers.

Autumn

The Siberian thrush leaves in September. It flies more than 2000 kilometres to South Asia.

As the days become shorter and colder, bean geese prepare for their migration 3000 kilometres south.

By July, the yellow warblers are ready to leave. They may fly more than 1500 kilometres.

Some yellow warblers stay less than three months!

The yellow warbler makes a small cup-shaped nest in a tree.

Seas and oceans

Seas and oceans are saltwater habitats. They vary from small, shallow, sheltered bays to vast, deep, stormy oceans.

Limpets cling tightly to the rocks as they feed on tiny plants.

The continental shelf is the area of sea bed around most land, about 100–200 metres deep.

The seashore is a harsh habitat – bashed by big waves, heated by the sun, soaked with rain and covered by high tides.

The **lobster** lurks in a cave and grabs passing victims.

Can you find these sea creatures? Write their names below.

Starfish use their 'arms' to pull apart shellfish before eating them.

The ocean surface waters are light, illuminated by sunlight.

The **marlin** is a speedy predator growing to 5 metres long.

The **Portuguese man o' war** is a group of jellyfish-like animals with a 'sail'.

The ocean's mid water becomes darker and colder.

The **megamouth shark** opens its jaws wide to swallow any kind of food.

Cod form large shoals (groups) that prey on any smaller creatures.

The **deep-sea angler** has a light on its head to attract victims.

On the deep sea bed, it is totally black and almost ice-cold.

101

Across the ocean

Some sea creatures travel farther than any land animal. Many have no nests, dens or regular homes. They roam for thousands of kilometres across the open ocean.

The **bottlenose dolphin** swims south in winter to warmer waters, then north again for the summer. Some of these journeys are more than 2000 kilometres.

How do sea animals find their way across vast oceans?

Pacific Ocean

North America

Atlantic Ocean

South America

The **grey whale** spends summer in cold but food-rich northern Pacific waters, and winter in warmer waters near the tropics. It's a yearly journey of over 20,000 kilometres.

Atlantic Ocean

The female **blue shark** travels across the Atlantic, from America to Europe, to have her babies. She then travels south to Africa, and back across the Atlantic to where she started – a round trip of 15,000 kilometres.

Write the animals in order, from who migrates the longest distance to who migrates the shortest distance.

1 ....grey whale.........................

2 ....

3 ....

4 ....

5 ....dugong...............................

Europe

They use positions of the Sun, Moon and stars to help them find their way!

Asia

Africa

The **dugong** or sea-cow is about 3 metres long. It swims over 1000 kilometres each year to feed on seagrass and other plants, always staying near the coast.

Indian Ocean

Pacific Ocean

Australia

The **green turtle** slowly wanders the ocean, flapping its flippers, to search for jellyfish and plants. In one year it can cover more than 6000 kilometres.

Great white shark

Water out through gill slits

Water flows over gills

Great white sharks can swim fast, but they cannot turn quickly or slow down suddenly.

Water in through mouth

The great white can detect the tiniest drops of blood in water. It follows the trail to a sick or injured victim.

ANIMAL FACT FILE

 Animal group: Fish

 Length: 6.5 metres

 Habitat: Coast to open sea

 Where in the world: All but the coldest oceans

 Main foods: Fish, seabirds, seals, dolphins, whales – anything!

 In danger?: Yes – vulnerable

It's a good job they can't turn quickly!

When a great white is seen from above, its dark top blends into the dark water below. When seen from below, its light underbelly blends with the sunlight above! Colour this great white.

This clever form of camouflage is called countershading!

These lines are gill slits. Water flows over the frilly gills just under them. This is how the shark breathes.

The great white has 50 teeth in the front row, but behind are another 200 or more. Each tooth behind is ready to move forwards if the tooth in front breaks off.

105

Between the tides

The seashore is an in-between habitat. It's dry when the tide is out and wet when the tide comes in. This happens twice each day, every day.

Low tide

The rocky shore animals hide away or close up. They must cope with sun, wind, rain, or even snow.

Beadlet anemones close up their tentacles when the tide is out.

Mussels cling to the rock using strong, stretchy threads.

Beadlet anemones look like jelly blobs at low tide!

High tide

The sea covers the shore. But it can be dangerous, with huge crashing waves that roll around rocks and pebbles.

The **peacock worm** sticks out its tentacles to sweep the water for bits of floating food.

At high tide, **barnacles** open the tops of their shells.

Beadlet anemones are all colours of the rainbow. Colour these red, orange, yellow, green, blue, indigo and violet!

Blue whale

Blue whales 'sing' by making clicks, squeaks and wails!

ANIMAL FACT FILE

 Animal group: Mammal

 Length: 30 metres

 Habitat: Open sea

 Where in the world: All oceans, even polar regions

 Main foods: Krill and other small creatures

 In danger?: Yes – endangered

On top of the whale's head are its blowholes (its breathing nostrils). They blow out old, stale air and take in fresh air.

Whale flippers are like our arms – they have bones inside. They can turn to steer when swimming.

Whale flukes are not like our legs – they do not have bones inside. They are mainly muscle.

The blue whale's throat has skin grooves or creases, called pleats.

Carefully cut out small krill shapes from card and put them in a sink full of water. Try using a kitchen sieve like a whale's baleen to scoop up the food. Can you catch them all in one go?

Whale calls travel hundreds of kilometres through the sea!

Long, brush-like parts, called baleen, hang from the whale's upper jaw, to sieve food from the water.

Blue whales eat small shrimp-like creatures called krill.

Battle of the giants

Many of the world's largest predators live in the ocean. When they meet, each must decide whether to attack and make a feast of its enemy, or leave to find smaller prey.

KILLER WHALE

HEADS	Length: 9 m
TAILS	Senses: 8/10

The killer whale is actually the biggest kind of dolphin. Its teeth lock together so no victim can escape.

Round 1

Winner:

....

TIGER SHARK

HEADS	Length: 5 m
TAILS	Senses: 9/10

The tiger shark is one of the largest and fiercest sharks. It attacks and eats almost any prey!

GIANT SPIDER CRAB

HEADS	Pincers: 10
TAILS	Width: 3 m

The giant spider crab has spindly pincers. It feeds on dead and dying creatures.

Round 2

Winner:

....

LION'S MANE JELLYFISH

HEADS	Tentacles: 100 +
TAILS	Width: 2 m

The lion's mane jellyfish is the biggest jellyfish, with stinging tentacles over 20 metres long.

SPERM WHALE

HEADS	Length: 20 m
TAILS	Eye size: 7 cm

The sperm whale is the world's largest predator. It has big cone-shaped teeth in its lower jaw.

VS

Winner:

....

COLOSSAL SQUID

HEADS	Length: 13 m
TAILS	Eye size: 27 cm

The colossal squid is the world's largest invertebrate. Its tentacles have suckers with sharp hooks.

Play 'Battle of the giants' with a friend! You'll need a coin and a pencil.

1. Pick your team: red or blue.

2. For each round, flip a coin to see what feature will win the battle.

3. Write the winner's name in the box.

4. Whoever wins the most rounds is the champion!

Champion:

....

Write the champion's name on the trophy and colour it in!

Tundra

Tundra is land that is frozen for much of the year. It is too cold for trees to grow, but low plants grow in the short summer.

The **rock ptarmigan** pecks up any bits of plant food, including seeds, stems and roots.

The **stoat** searches for small creatures such as mice, voles and lemmings.

In the winter, white fur and feathers blend into the snow and ice!

The **snowshoe hare** eats twigs, bark from trees, and buds from plants and flowers.

112

Summer

Tundra swans feed on the plants, make nests and raise their chicks. In just a few weeks, they will fly south on their winter migration.

Melted ice and snow forms pools of water where **mosquitoes** and other insects breed in their billions.

But, look! In the summer, they shed their white coats and grow brown ones instead!

🔍 Can you spot a...

rock ptarmigan?

stoat?

snowshoe hare?

Big and small

The tundra is a dangerous place for plant-eaters, because predators are always hungry. These two animals, one big and one small, have different ways to avoid becoming prey.

Among the biggest tundra animals are musk oxen. Some weigh almost 500 kilograms!

Musk oxen live in small groups, called herds, usually from five to ten, but sometimes up to fifty.

Musk oxen

When in danger, adults stand in a circle around their young, known as calves, to protect them.

Both male and females have horns. They use them to scare enemies, and to battle each other to be boss of the herd.

One of the smallest tundra mammals is the tundra vole. It is only 15 centimetres long.

The tundra vole is a rodent – cousin of mice, rats, hamsters and gerbils.

When in danger, tundra voles race to their nest burrow. They may block the entrance with earth to keep out predators.

Its long, sharp front teeth never stop growing!

Tundra vole

These three voles want to get back to their own nest burrows. Can you help them find the right tunnels?

Snowy owl

Its eyes see well in the dark. The owl moves its head from side to side to work out how far away things are.

The owl's hearing is amazing – it can even hear hidden prey burrowing under the snow.

ANIMAL FACT FILE

Animal group: Bird

Height: 60 centimetres

Habitat: Tundra, rocky areas, coasts and grasslands

Where in the world: North America, Europe and Asia

Main foods: Small creatures such as lemmings, voles, mice, birds

In danger?: Not yet

An adult male has white plumage (feathers), while the female and youngsters have brown markings.

To catch prey, it swoops down and grasps its victim in its long foot claws, known as talons.

Even the feet have thick feathers!

A snowy owl mostly hunts at night. But when it has chicks to feed, it flies by day too.

Join the dots to see who is waiting back at the snowy owl's nest.

Happy families

The tundra summer is so short that animals raise their families fast. Youngsters must grow up quickly to survive the long, cold winter ahead!

The Arctic tern flies from the Arctic to the Antarctic and back each year.

Pikas may look like mice, but they are cousins of rabbits and hares. A female and male have four or five babies in late spring.

An **Arctic tern** lays two eggs in a nest lined with grass and moss, near the coast. Both parents attack any creature that comes near the eggs or chicks.

Draw your own family photo!

The **snow bunting's** eggs hatch in less than two weeks, and the chicks can fly only two weeks later!

The **Arctic hare** does not have a nest burrow. Instead, it shelters among plants. The female has up to 10 babies, called leverets.

Caribou

ANIMAL FACT FILE

 Animal group: Mammal

 Height: 1.5 metres

 Habitat: Tundra, conifer forests

 Where in the world: North America, Europe and Asia

Main foods: Leaves, grasses, lichens, moss and other plants

 In danger?: Not yet

Both male and female caribou have antlers. In all other deer, the female lacks antlers.

Each year, the caribou grows new antlers. They develop in the spring or summer, and fall off in autumn or winter.

In Europe, the caribou is called the reindeer.

The long hairs of the caribou's outer coat are hollow to help keep the cold out and body warmth in.

Caribou click as they walk! The sound is made by bones and joints in their feet. It may help the herd stay together when it is dark.

Put your hands over your eyes. Ask a friend to walk around the room, clicking their fingers every five seconds. Point to where you think they are. Were you right?

In summer, the hooves are wide and soft for walking in the swampy tundra ground.

In winter, the hooves become hard and sharp-edged to grip snow and ice.

Mountain tundra

As you go up a mountain, it gets colder and windier. Up high, there is alpine (mountain) tundra. It is home to some of the world's best climbers.

Soaring in the sky is the **bearded vulture**. Its main food is carrion – the bodies of animals that have died.

For every 1000 metres you go straight up, the temperature drops by 10°C!

No wonder alpine tundra is rarely warmer than 10°C, even in summer.

Above the mountain tundra, it is too cold and windy for plants. There are just bare rocks and the snowy mountain top.

At breeding time, male **black grouse** strut, show off their feathers and make loud calls to attract females.

Alpine marmots can dig their burrow in soil that is very hard or even frozen!

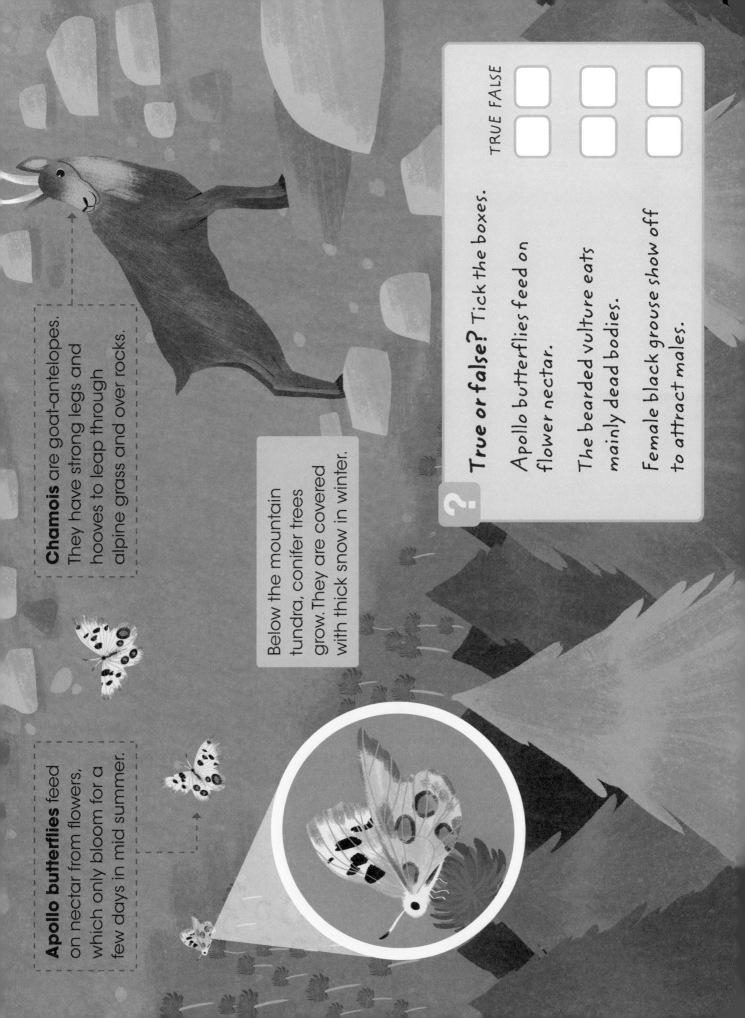

Chamois are goat-antelopes. They have strong legs and hooves to leap through alpine grass and over rocks.

Apollo butterflies feed on nectar from flowers, which only bloom for a few days in mid summer.

Below the mountain tundra, conifer trees grow. They are covered with thick snow in winter.

True or false? Tick the boxes.

TRUE FALSE

Apollo butterflies feed on flower nectar.

The bearded vulture eats mainly dead bodies.

Female black grouse show off to attract males.

Glossary

Amphibians Cold-blooded animals without scaly skin that can live in water or on land.

Birds Warm-blooded animals with feathers, wings and a beak. They lay eggs that hatch into chicks. Many make nests for their eggs.

Breed To make more of an animal's kind. Some animals lay eggs. Others give birth to babies.

Camouflage A colour, pattern or shape of an animal that helps it to blend in with its surroundings.

Canopy The uppermost branches of the trees in a forest.

Carnivore A class of animals that feeds on the flesh of other animals.

Cold-blooded Cold-blooded animals become hotter when it is hot outside and cooler when it is cold outside.

Down The soft, fine, fluffy feathers or hair that form the insulating undercoat layer.

Emergent The tallest trees in a forest, which grow above the canopy.

Feathers Soft structures growing from a bird's skin and forming its plumage.

Filter-feed Feeding by filtering or sieving out tiny plankton or nutrients floating in the water.

Fish Animals with scaly skin, gills for breathing underwater, and fins and a tail for swimming. They live in water.

Food chain A series of individual plants or animals, each dependent on the next as a source of food.

Freshwater Relating to or living in freshwater – the water in rivers and lakes.

Habitat A type of place where an animal or plant lives. It provides the right conditions for that living thing to thrive, such as food, temperature and amount of water.

Herbivore A class of animals that doesn't feed on flesh, but that eats only vegetable or plant matter.

Hibernation A deep sleep that some animals enter to conserve energy and survive harsh conditions.

Insulation Not allowing heat or cold to pass through.

Invertebrate An animal without a backbone. Worms, insects, spiders, crabs and starfish are invertebrates.

Mammals Warm-blooded animals with fur or hair that produce milk to feed their babies. Humans are mammals – so are dogs and dolphins.

Metamorphosis Changing shape greatly when growing from young to adult – for example, a caterpillar changing into a butterfly.

Migration A seasonal movement of animals from one place to another.

Omnivore A type of animal that gets energy from eating both the flesh of other animals and plants or vegetables. Humans are omnivores.

Pinniped A carnivorous aquatic mammal, such as a seal or walrus.

Plumage The layer of feathers covering the body of a bird.

Predator A meat-eating animal that hunts and kills other animals to eat. The animals it hunts are known as prey.

Prey An animal that is hunted and killed for food by another animal. The animal that hunts it is known as a predator.

Primate A mammal distinguished by having hand-like feet and forward-facing eyes. Monkeys, apes and humans are primates.

Reptiles Cold-blooded animals that have dry, scaly skin, and that lay eggs on land. Snakes, lizards, crocodiles and turtles are all types of reptile.

Saltwater Relating to or living in saltwater – the water in the sea.

Scales Tough, overlapping plates that cover and protect the skin of reptiles and fish.

Senses An animal's senses tell it about the world around it.

Shoal A large number of fish swimming together.

Undercoat An inner layer of short, fine fur or down underlying an animal's outer fur or feathers, providing warmth and waterproofing.

Understorey The lower branches of the trees in a forest.

Venom A harmful liquid made by some predators to help them kill or hurt their prey. Usually injected through teeth, fangs or a sting.

Vertebrate An animal with a backbone. Amphibians, birds, mammals and reptiles are vertebrates.

Warm-blooded Warm-blooded animals stay the same temperature, regardless of whether it is hot or cold outside.

Index

Answers

Page 9
Bird, Fish, Mammal

Pages 12–13

Page 17
1 – Barbet
2 – Woodpecker
3 – Honeyguide

Page 23
1 – Monkey (howler monkey)
2 – Ape (orang-utan)
3 – Ape (gorilla)
4 – Monkey (spider monkey)

Page 27
American bison, Hyena,
Saker falcon

Pages 28–29
Wildebeest – Fresh grass
African wild dogs – Home den
Thomson's gazelles – Waterhole

Page 37
Giant anteater – Termites
Darkling beetle – Grass seeds
Lion – Grant's gazelle

Page 46
False, False, True, False

Page 49

Page 51
There are 14 krill

Page 52

Page 57
Rhea – 1.4 m
Cassowary – 1.7 m
Emu – 1.9 m

Pages 58–59
Termites – Nest
Barking gecko – Rock
Namib sidewinder – Burrow

Page 61
Dromedary, Bactrian, Dromedary,
Bactrian

Page 65

Pages 70–71

Page 73

Page 75
False, True, False

Pages 82–83

Pages 88–89

Page 97
There are 16 salmon

Page 100
Deep-sea angler, Portuguese
man o' war, Limpets, Lobster

Page 103
1 – Grey whale
2 – Blue shark
3 – Green turtle
4 – Bottlenose dolphin
5 – Dugong

Page 113

Page 115

Page 123
True, True, False